WALKING IN
THE SHOES
OF ANOTHER

WALKING IN
THE SHOES
OF ANOTHER

Stories for seeing life
from different perspectives

LARS COLLMAR
Translated by Lesley Gleeson

HINTONHOUSE

First published in 2010 by
Hinton House Publishers Ltd, Newman House, 4 High Street,
Buckingham, MK18 1NT, UK
T +44 (0)1280 822557 F +44 (0) 560 3135274
E info@hintonpublishers.co.uk

www.hintonpublishers.co.uk

British Library Cataloguing in Publication Data
Collmar, Lars, 1939–
    Walking in the shoes of another : stories for seeing life
    from different perspectives.
    1. Social intelligence–Study and teaching (Elementary)–
    Activity programs–Great Britain.
    I. Title
    372.8'2'044'0941-dc22

ISBN-13: 978 1 906531 24 9

Printed and bound in the United Kingdom by Hobbs the Printers Ltd

Original edition published in Swedish under the title *Två par mockasiner*
by Argument Förlag AB, Sweden.
© 2004 Argument Förlag AB och Lars Collmar

Contents

Introduction

"Do not judge another until you have walked a mile in his moccasins" – so says an old Native-American proverb. The idea of *Walking in the Shoes of Another* is to stimulate and practice the idea of trying to see things from another person's perspective.

How often do we quickly judge a person and what they stand for, and then later, when we find out more, realise that the picture is much more complex than we had originally thought?

Many misunderstandings and preconceptions could be avoided if we just try to communicate more with each other. History has shown us that conflict, and perhaps even war, can be avoided as long as dialogue is maintained. The parties involved may be angry and hostile but as long as there is discussion there is no fighting.

Walking in the Shoes of Another aims to stimulate discussion, discussion that, it is hoped, will encourage and develop young people's ability to view events from different perspectives.

Using *Walking in the Shoes of Another* should prove to be fun and stimulating. Working with this material will help young people to be more curious about what lies behind a situation, and instead of rushing to judge they may perhaps look for what is hidden behind peoples' opinions, behaviour and reactions and this will encourage discussion instead of leading to conflict.

This resource is intended for use with young people aged from eight to twelve, with some stories being more suitable for younger pupils and some for older. However, all groups are different and the book is flexible enough to be adapted as appropriate.

In this book, ten social situations are depicted. Each chapter consists of two stories describing the same event from two different perspectives. Following each of the two stories is a set of questions designed to stimulate lively discussion, and a final set of questions to answer after both stories have been read will allow groups to compare the experiences of both characters.

Suggestions for Use

These sets of stories can be used in whole-class groups, small groups or on a one-to-one basis.

Read one of the stories to the group and then discuss the relevant questions. Now read the second story, does the picture change? Discuss the questions relating to the second story and then the questions for both stories. It is not until both stories have been read that the complete picture is revealed. What can we do to be better at seeing the whole picture in life generally?

Questions can be answered individually or used as a basis for groupwork and whole-group discussions. Groups could be divided into two, and each given one of the stories to read and discuss. Then each small group could prepare answers to the questions relating to their story for a whole-group presentation and discussion.

Discussion & Follow Up

Discuss different situations where we risk knowing only half or a part of the truth.

◆ What can be done about this?

◆ Is it always necessary to know everything?

◆ When do we tell half-truths?

◆ When might we do this consciously and when might we do it subconsciously?

◆ Can we avoid half-truths or white lies?

◆ Is there ever any justification in not telling the whole truth?

An effective way of practicing seeing a situation from different perspectives is to ask pupils to write their own stories, describing the same situation with two different viewpoints, for example, two players describing the same football match. A third version could include the referee's point of view.

Other ideas for story pairs could include:

Friend – Friend
Teacher – Pupil
Parent – Child
Girl – Boy

Another variant could be to let a group describe a situation they've experienced together, or a play, a film, or half-an-hour in the playground.

Compare these stories. Do different people emphasise different things in their experiences and, if so, why?

Like a Yellow Butterfly

Eve

It was the last day of school and a bright sunny day. Eve had a new dress for the occasion, a wonderful lemon-yellow dress, which had really been a bit too expensive, but Mum had bought it anyway. It was a bit stiff, exactly as a good new dress should be when it's just come from the shop and before its first wash. It smelled good too, well, maybe not good exactly, but crisp. It had a little sharp smell, which meant 'absolutely new'.

"Be careful of your new dress!" Mum had called as she left home that morning. It hadn't been necessary, Eve hardly dared to move, she was so aware of her dress. The other girls in her class had dressed up as well, but Eve looked the best, really she did, and Jasmine said so too.

"You look great!", she said. "No-one looks as pretty as you today."

"Oh, thank you", said Eve, and quickly complimented Jasmine on her own dress, because she knew that's what she should do. But both girls knew that Eve's dress was the most beautiful.

"You look just like a yellow butterfly", said Jasmine, and Eve floated happily round the school playground, being very careful not to bump into something that might mark her new dress.

Then the end of term celebrations began. The school orchestra played as they all walked in to the assembly hall. The choir went in first and then the whole school followed, starting with the youngest classes. The sun blinked in the corner and shone on Eve's dress. It was the first day of the summer holiday!

Eve's class sat right at the front of the hall. The sudden coolness in the hall made everything seem serious. The room was so big and the ceilings so high that everyone moved quietly and hardly dared whisper, but once class after class had filed in, the room seemed to shrink and become friendlier. At the same time the hushed whispering became louder and louder. Soon there were only a few empty chairs right at the back. These last few places were for parents and relatives to compete for as best they could. Suddenly, the huge room was full to bursting.

Now it was the turn of Eve's class to sing for everyone, and her stomach churned. Thank goodness she wasn't singing a solo, she would have felt awful! It was bad enough that her class had to start all the singing. Eve was standing right at the front of the choir, in the first row, so that everyone saw her lemon-yellow dress (not, she thought, that it was important, but everyone could see it). She tried to find Mum and Grandma and her little brother (Dad was at work) but she couldn't see them in the crowd.

Their song went well, and then it was over. There was a bit of pushing when they all returned to their places – "Watch my dress!", she thought – and then the other classes sang and the headmaster made his speech, and then the deputy head. And then they all sang the school song and at last it was the summer holidays!

Eve ran out into the sunshine as soon as she could. Everyone was looking for their families and running in different directions. The girls were all hugging each other, saying goodbye, Eve was too, very carefully because of her dress, but Jasmine, Caroline and Sophie would get their goodbye hug. Just as they were about to say goodbye Sophie turned, "Oh, no!", she cried. "What's happened to your dress?"

"What do you mean?", asked Eve, confused.

"There, in the middle of your back. You've got a huge chocolate stain! Oh no, what a shame!", said Sophie. (Except she didn't actually look that sorry about it.)

Eve twisted and turned, trying desperately to see the mark but couldn't see anything. Now Caroline and Jasmine were commenting and pointing too, so Eve carefully took her arms out of the dress and turned it round on her body.

Then she saw it! A great, big, brown print of sticky chocolate, just below the neck on the back of her dress.

Her friends were very sympathetic.

"How did that happen?"

"It must be chocolate."

"Really sticky!"

"You can even see a print from someone's lips."

"I know what happened", said Caroline. "It was Simon. It must have been Simon! He was standing right behind you when we were singing, and now I remember that he was eating something."

"That disgusting pig!", said Sophie. "He's always got sweets in his mouth, even when we're going to sing!"

"It's just too much", complained Caroline. "How can you be so clumsy that you don't realise that you're slobbering chocolate on someone's dress?"

Jasmine looked the most angry.

"It wasn't clumsiness", she said seriously. "It was pure meanness, he did it on purpose, I saw him."

And she started to explain.

"I didn't realise what was happening at first because we were all singing. But he was in the second row, right behind Eve and I was in the second row too. There was only Lisa between me and Simon so I could see him really well. Suddenly, he leant forward towards Eve, as if he was wiping his mouth on her dress. Didn't you notice, Eve?"

Eve, who was almost in tears, couldn't answer. She just shook her head.

"Well, that's what he did anyway." said Jasmine decidedly. "I'm sure of it. I remember perfectly. Except I didn't realise he'd stained your dress, and then I forgot about it."

"Do you really think that he did it on purpose?", whispered all the girls, except for Eve who just looked really miserable. "But that's so awful."

Jasmine nodded.

"First he looked to the side, to make sure that no-one had seen him, then he pulled a face and leaned forwards and then back again. He did it on purpose, I'm sure of it."

The mystery was solved. Simon had ruined Eve's new dress out of sheer meanness. They wanted to get hold of him and ask him why he had done it, but he'd already disappeared. He was probably sitting on his own somewhere, stuffing himself with sweets and feeling pleased at having destroyed Eve's beautiful lemon-yellow dress.

But why had he done it? Why would anyone want to destroy something and make someone sad?

Like a Yellow Butterfly

Questions for Eve's story

1 Is it wrong to let people know that you think you look pretty?
If so, why?

2 Is it possible for someone to want to spoil something on purpose?
What might they be thinking or feeling, if so?

3 Why do you think Simon leaned forward towards Eve's dress?

4 What do you think he would have said if the girls had challenged
him and asked him what had happened?

5 Will the dress ever be as good again, even if it is washed carefully?

Like a Yellow Butterfly

Simon

Simon had a big secret that no-one knew – he always had a crush on someone. Sometimes it was a girl at school. It was usually someone in his class but it could be a girl he saw in the park or who lived close by. In the summer it was a girl he met on holiday. The actual person changed, but there was always someone.

But it was his secret. It would have been really embarrassing if anyone found out; worse than embarrassing.

Simon knew that some idiots in his class told the girls they liked them and they giggled and whispered and passed notes to each other across the classroom. It was so stupid, he'd rather die than do anything like that.

Now it was the last day of term and the sun was frying the playground. In the past few days it had suddenly become summer and as soon as they'd finished school Simon and his family were going on holiday. Then it would be only three weeks and two days until his birthday. He'd asked for a pet rabbit for his birthday and he was pretty sure he was going to get one. Life couldn't have been better!

"Rachel the rabbit", he whispered to himself. Rachel was a girl in his class who he had a crush on at the moment and that's why he wanted a cuddly rabbit for

7

his birthday. Of course, when he was on holiday Kristen would be there as usual.

Then love struck him in a flash. There, in the middle of the playground with the classes all lined up to go into assembly, love struck him.

It was Eve, of course, why hadn't he noticed her before? Even though they'd been in the same class for ages he'd never thought of her! Unbelievable! She looked amazing, the way she fluttered round the playground in her new yellow dress. Like a yellow butterfly, so beautiful and so pretty.

He tried not to show his feelings but made sure that he was standing just behind her. Then some idiot came and squeezed in between them. Simon didn't show how disappointed he felt, instead, he just took a big piece of chocolate from his pocket and put it in his mouth. Simon loved to eat sweets, especially when he had strong feelings.

The school orchestra began to play, all the classes started moving and the sun lit up Eve's yellow butterfly dress.

Then it was time to start singing. Their class had to sing first. This time Simon managed to get a place right behind Eve. He stood as close as he could so that he could smell the scent of her hair – very carefully, he breathed in, her shampoo smelt of fresh meadows.

He felt weak with happiness. He was standing so close to her and she didn't suspect a thing. Only Simon knew how very much he loved her. Carefully, he took another piece of chocolate out of his pocket. He just had to have another piece of chocolate even if it made it difficult to sing the song.

At first it was enough just to be standing close to Eve, but after a while he became bolder. On the back of her dress, just below the neck was a big golden-yellow pattern. If he was very careful he could place a kiss, as light as a butterfly, on the pattern without her noticing. He was sure he could do it.

Quickly, he looked from side to side. The coast was clear, everyone was busy singing. He leaned his head forwards and then back again with lightening speed and kissed the golden pattern. He had done it and she hadn't noticed a thing!

Then he saw it. A very clear print of his lips, in chocolate, right in the middle of the design. A cold hand twisted his stomach.

"It's my fault!", he wanted to shout out in the middle of the song. "It's my fault, but I did it because I like her so much!" Maybe he should go round to her house after school and own up and apologise?

Just as her angry mum would be about to tell her off for spoiling the new dress, Simon would ring her doorbell and rush in and say, "Stop! It's not her fault, it's mine! Tell me off instead!"

But you can't do things like that. So Simon kept quiet, and chewed and chewed on his chocolate. But however many he ate he couldn't get rid of the twisting pain in his stomach.

Like a Yellow Butterfly

Questions for Simon's story

1 Why does Simon never tell any of the girls that he likes them?

2 Is it possible to really like someone but to manage never to show it?

3 Do feelings show anyway, however hard you try to hide them?

4 Why does Simon eat so many sweets and chocolates?

5 Do you think Simon will ever tell Eve who really marked her dress?

6 Would he be able to explain that it was an accident?

Like a Yellow Butterfly

Questions for both stories

1 Do you think Simon would have confessed to the girls how he felt about Eve if they'd found him and accused him of being mean?

2 Is it really that difficult to tell people how you feel? Why do you think this is?

3 Is it always possible to know why someone acts the way they do?

4 Do you always know why you do things yourself?

The Sweet Shop

Oliver

As always during the lunch break there were loads of people in the sweet shop, but Oliver wasn't in a hurry, he wasn't even sure if he was going to buy anything. You weren't really allowed to go there during school hours, but no-one really cared – not even the teachers. The little shop was so nice to be in, it was cool in the summer and warm in the winter and it smelt so good. It always put Oliver in a good mood when he took a deep breath and filled his nostrils with the sweet smell. Sometimes he bought something, sometimes he didn't, depending on how much money he had.

It was just nice to walk around and see what they had. The whistles made of caramel looked really good, he hadn't seen them before. He wondered if they actually made any sound when you blew them. Without thinking he picked one up and went to put it into his mouth to try but stopped himself just in time. Of course, you weren't allowed to try them out before you bought one! He looked at the whistle in his hand and was just about to put it back when a huge pair of hands grabbed him by the shoulders.

"Don't touch the sweets!"

Oliver froze.

Panic shot through his body until he realised that
it was just the old man who owned the shop.
Then he was insulted. What had got into the old
man? He was usually so kind and friendly.

"I'm tired of you shoplifters!", shouted the shopkeeper. "You never buy anything, you just hang around and fill your pockets. Well, now I've had enough!"

Even though he was totally innocent Oliver felt guilty, but he couldn't understand why. He hadn't tried to blow the caramel whistle, he'd just picked it up and held it in his hand. That couldn't be a crime, and he definitely hadn't decided to steal it – he certainly wasn't a thief! Even so, he felt like a thief who'd been caught red-handed. He tried unsuccessfully to squirm loose.

"Leave me alone", he said. "I haven't done anything, it's OK."

Then the old man really started to have a go. "Oh, so it's OK, is it?", he mimicked, "It's OK for a load of horrible kids to steal from me! It's OK for you to stand there and eat my sweets and fill your pockets when you think I'm not looking, and ... and ... of course it's OK isn't it? Well, let me tell you that it's **not** OK. I saw what you did and now it's time to call the police. That's how OK it is!"

A little ring of spectators had gathered round them.

"So you got caught then", said an older boy with a superior look, "anyway, those whistles taste really disgusting."

Oliver felt sick and ready to cry all at once, but he wasn't going to show it. He wasn't going to give them that pleasure. He bit his lip and tried to look as cool as he could. After all, he hadn't actually done anything wrong.

"But I haven't done anything", he repeated again and again. "It's the truth. I was just looking at the caramel whistles."

"Are you going to buy one then?", shouted the old man angrily.

"Disgustingly horrible", said the older boy again.

"No, I don't think so", whispered Oliver, but unfortunately he sounded really pitiful.

"Then get out of here!", screamed the old man. "And never come back again if you're not going to buy anything!"

Oliver stood uncertainly in the middle of the shop. The owner had let go of his shoulders and had obviously forgotten his threat to call the police. Or maybe he wasn't so sure any more. How could he be, Oliver hadn't actually done anything. Maybe the old man had begun to realise that it was all a misunderstanding.

"I didn't do anything. I'm telling the truth", mumbled Oliver. He felt he had to say it. He felt someone pushing him out of the shop and he tripped and fell on the doorstep. Quickly he picked himself up and rushed out into the street.

Once he was outside, Oliver felt the tears and hate rushing through his body.

How he hated that disgusting, horrible old man. He would never go back into the stinking shop ever again!

Oliver felt sick. For a moment he wondered if he should go back to the shop and be sick right into one of those boxes filled with chocolates, raspberry jellies and wine gums. That would serve the old man right. But of course he didn't. He just walked slowly back to school. His stomach ached and he hated the old man in the sweet shop as much as an ten-year-old boy can hate anyone!

The Sweet Shop

Questions for Oliver's story

1 Do you know an old fashioned sweet shop like this? What's it like?

2 Which is worse, being accused when you're guilty or being accused when you're innocent?

3 Is it possible to feel guilty if you're accused of something, even though you aren't guilty?

4 Is it important to pretend that you're not affected when someone shouts at you? Does it affect you?

5 Why is it so important to Oliver that the shopkeeper believes what he says?

6 Can young people really feel hate? When? How does it feel?

7 Why do you think the old man was so angry?

8 Should Oliver just try to forget his bad experience or can he do something about it?

The Sweet Shop

Alfie

The attack last night hadn't been that dangerous really!

Alfie had been standing behind the counter of the sweetshop as usual. He liked it there. He liked talking to the customers, and the fact that there was a school just over the road wasn't a bad thing either. Children like sweets and every break time a whole crowd of pupils would flock over to the shop. Not everyone bought something, but lots of them did and there was life and movement in the little shop. Alfie liked that. But that was before the attack!

He had come in just before closing time, a small, long-haired boy. Even though there was just him and Alfie in the shop the boy began filling his pockets with sweets. Was he stupid or something?

"Hey! You boy! What do you think you're doing?", Alfie had said, and laid a heavy hand on the boy's shoulder, in a firm but not completely unfriendly manner. Alfie was a friendly man at heart.

But then the boy pulled out a knife and lunged at Alfie's chest right at his heart! In a reflex action Alfie quickly flung up his arms in front of himself and the knife just caught his jacket and gave him a small cut on his arm. Then the boy rushed out of the shop and Alfie was left holding his injured arm and looking confused. A young lad, who couldn't have been more than fourteen or fifteen, probably on drugs or drunk, and he had lunged straight towards Alfie's heart. What was the world coming to?

Alfie calmed down and called the police. Eventually, a police car came and they took down the evidence and even drove Alfie to casualty. One of the policemen had advised Alfie to ask the hospital for an appointment with a counsellor, the shock of the attack would probably hit him a bit later, the man said.

Well! Alfie didn't think much of counselling and after all it was only a little cut. Even if the boy had aimed for his heart – and he had – Alfie had managed to get his arms up really quickly, pure reflex, and the worst damage had been done to his old jacket.

After three hours of waiting in casualty Alfie was fed up with sitting there. He left the hospital and made his way home where he bandaged the cut himself. So really, it had been no big deal. Nothing serious anyway, thanks to Alfie's quick reflexes.

But that night he couldn't sleep! He didn't want to admit it to himself but he was afraid, really afraid. In his mind, he went over what had happened again and again. Then he went over and over what might have happened if he hadn't had such quick reflexes. Most of all he couldn't stop thinking about what might happen in the future.

19

He might be stabbed at any time by any kid who happened to come in. Every time the bell on the door jingled it could be an attacker walking into the shop and Alfie wasn't sure he would manage to get his arms up in time if it happened again. Your reflexes don't work as well when you're frozen with fear. And he was! Alfie hated to admit it, but it he was simply petrified.

When the alarm clock went off the next morning, without him having had a wink of sleep, his first thought was to stay at home. He was his own boss and he could afford to take a few days off until he felt a bit better again. Then he began to think of the Biggles books he had read as a child, and how a pilot who crashed should always get straight back into a plane and fly, right away, otherwise he'd never fly again. So Alfie trudged off to the sweet shop.

This is good he thought to himself, Biggles therapy, much better than a counsellor. But the hours dragged. Shouldn't he be feeling better soon? Surely his legs shouldn't still be shaking. When will my body realise that I'm not afraid, he asked himself?

The morning dragged by. Alfie started shivering and then sweating.

"I don't care", he whispered to himself, "I'll be like Biggles and start again, but shouldn't this blasted plane be taking off soon?"

Then it was afternoon and lunch break at the school. The sweetshop filled up with pupils and Alfie was still feeling a bit shaky. When would everything start feeling normal again? It wasn't like this in Biggles.

Then Alfie saw him – the little knife-wielding kid.

He was standing by the new caramel whistles and picked one up and hid it in his hand. Now he would put it straight into his pocket. Alfie was feeling faint. He wanted to shout at them all, "take anything you want! Just don't hurt me!" Then, finally, the plane took off. The weight and the fear disappeared and he felt his courage come back to him. He flew across the shop helped by a wonderful release of anger. No little kid, with or without a knife, would ever scare him again! As soon as he put his hand on the boy's shoulder, Alfie realised it was the wrong boy but his anger didn't disappear, the boy was a shoplifter and now he'd learn his lesson!

Alfie stormed about shouting for a long time before he threw the boy out of the door. His arm was aching a bit, but he actually felt quite good. Now he was back to his old self again. He had conquered the most dangerous enemy of all, his own fear. He had recaptured the sweet shop and, at the same time, control of his own life.

21

The Sweet Shop

Questions for Alfie's story

1 Alfie wasn't afraid until the night after the attack. Have you ever been in a dangerous situation where you haven't felt afraid until afterwards?

2 Do you think it's true that a pilot who crashes should fly again as soon as possible?

3 What do you think would have happened if Alfie had taken a few days sick leave?

4 Is it possible to overcome fear by defying it? Have you ever tried this? How did you do it and what happened?

5 It is good to be brave if you aren't afraid, but what is bravery?

6 Alfie conquers his fear with anger. Do you think people often show anger to stop themselves from being afraid? Is this a good thing?

7 Was it a good thing that Alfie threw the boy out of the shop? Why?

8 Are you sure that the boy really was a shoplifter?

The Sweet Shop

Questions for both stories

1 Do you think that Alfie has any idea what Oliver is thinking and feeling? Does he realise how angry and confused Oliver is?

2 Would it help if Oliver could explain this to him? Would it be best if he explained straight away or later when everything has quietened down?

3 Could the opposite be true? Would Oliver be able to understand how Alfie felt if Alfie tried to explain to him?

4 Why is it so difficult to talk about our feelings? Would both Oliver and Alfie would have difficulty explaining how they felt inside?

5 Could Alfie and Oliver both be feeling the same thing? If so, what might it be?

6 Why do you think the shoplifter had a knife with him?

7 What is a fair way to deal with a shoplifter?

8 Do we have the right to be angry? How angry? Are there different rules for children and adults?

9 Is there any chance that Oliver and the shop keeper can be friends? How might that be possible?

Whose Fault – Mum's or Dad's?

Mum

Mum and Dad were in the kitchen arguing.

They didn't often argue, so it felt really bad that they were arguing now. Erin lay in bed and burrowed her head under the pillow so that she couldn't hear what they were saying. It didn't help though – there was only a thin door between the kitchen and her bedroom and the angry voices came right into her room. She tried to think of something good – it would be her ninth birthday in just a week. Mum had promised she could have a pizza party – not just the usual children's party, but the voices from the kitchen broke all her good thoughts into pieces.

She tried to ignore everything and just go to sleep but she couldn't do it. Dad and Mum were talking really quietly now, all she could hear were mumbled voices but she knew straight away that they were still arguing. She couldn't help straining her ears to listen, even though she didn't want to hear.

Dad was doing most of the talking. His voice was even and calm and you could tell he was trying to be friendly, but she wasn't fooled. He always sounded strained like that when he was angry but didn't want to show it.

25

Mum kept interrupting him again and again, but he just kept mumbling and explaining whatever it was he was trying to explain. Mum was easier to hear.

"… but you can't mean …", said Mum

"Mumble, mumble, mumble", said Dad.

"How long for?", asked Mum.

"Mumble", said Dad quickly.

"… and I knew nothing about it …"

"But I'm telling you now!", said Dad. And now he couldn't hide how angry he was.

"So Erin and I don't mean anything thing to you any more?", Mum almost screamed the words out.

"Mumble please, mumble, mumble, mumble." Dad tried to calm her down. "You must realise yourself that mumble, mumble, mumble?"

"Yes, well, leave then!", shouted Mum. "I won't hold you back. Take all your things and go to her! Do it and then you'll see how mumble, mumble, mumble."

And then Dad, quieter but just as angry, "take it easy, mumble, mumble, you'll wake Erin up."

It sounded as if they were hissing at each other, and then it was quiet, no more voices, just lots of angry noises. Cups being banged down on the table, the fridge door being slammed shut. Dad puffing a bit as he tried to get the suitcase down from the top shelf in the wardrobe, and then footsteps going backwards and forwards, backwards and forwards through the flat. And then the front door being slammed shut, really hard. Then silence! Total silence and the anger in the air started to disappear.

Mum opened the door to Erin's room and came over to tuck her in.

"Are you asleep?", she whispered.

Erin pretended to be asleep.

"I have to tell you something that isn't very nice", said Mum in a kind, sad voice.

"I don't want to hear", said Erin, "I'm asleep."

"Dad's moved out", said Mum. "He's fallen in love with another woman and now he's moving out to go and live with her instead."

"But he'll come back, won't he?", whispered Erin.

Mum snorted. "We can forget that", she said harshly, "he can only think of her and the baby they're going to have together. Yes, they're going to have a baby too; it's all cosy so he won't have time for us any more."

"But he still likes us, doesn't he?", whispered Erin.

"He has nothing against you", said Mum harshly, "but he hates me. He'll probably take you to the zoo every now and again, if he has time. He'll be very busy now you see!"

Erin started to cry.

"Don't be sad love", said Mum and hugged her hard. "You and I can look after ourselves. It'll be fine, don't you think? And I'll never leave you, I promise you that."

Then Mum started to cry too and Erin felt so sorry for her that she felt she should comfort her. How could Dad do this? It was all his fault, adults who were married weren't supposed to go and fall in love. It was disgusting. It wasn't right that someone should make anyone as unhappy as he'd made Mum. There should be a law against it.

"He's stupid", whispered Erin, "but we'll manage without him. We'll just forget about him."

"You're so sensible Erin", whispered Mum. "Everything will be fine, you'll see. Go to sleep now and don't be sad. Everything will look better in the morning."

And she left the room and closed the door quietly behind her.

Whose Fault – Mum's or Dad's?

Questions for Mum's story

1 Does it feel dangerous when your parents argue?

2 Do you feel you need to worry about it or should you just let them get on with it?

3 Erin doesn't want to hear their argument but she still strains her ears to listen. Why?

4 Is it possible to tell if someone's angry by their tone of voice, even when they try not to show it?

5 Why doesn't Erin want to hear what Mum comes in to tell her?

6 Whose fault is it that Erin's Mum and Dad are splitting up?

7 Is it disgusting when grown ups or parents fall in love with someone else?

8 Why does Erin say that they should just forget about her Dad?

9 How do you think she feels when she says that?

Whose Fault – Mum's or Dad's?

Dad

Suddenly Dad was standing in the kitchen.

At first Erin felt warm with happiness, she was so glad to see him. Dad. She wanted to throw herself into his arms. Then she remembered and became stiff all over. He had moved out. Now he lived with another woman and they were even going to have a baby together. He didn't care about Erin and her mum any more. He hadn't even bothered to come to see her on her birthday. That's how it was. How could she have forgotten that for even one second?

But what was he doing here now? It was the middle of the afternoon and Erin had just come home from school. Mum was still at work.

"Erin, I've missed you so much", said Dad. "I just came to get a few papers. I'm so glad that you're at home. Don't I get a kiss?"

Once again Erin wanted to run into his arms, but she stopped herself. It wasn't right after what he had done to Mum. She and Mum must stick together – as Mum kept saying, they only had each other now.

"Hi", said Erin quietly and then she went to her room and closed the door.

"Erin, wait", said Dad, "I want to talk to you. Can I come in?"

"No, you can't", said Erin through the door, "because you're stupid."

"Maybe I am", said Dad, "but I'd still like to talk to you. Can I?"

He tried the door handle, but Erin held on to the other side as hard as she could until Dad let go. Then he went away.

"Good", thought Erin. "I don't want to see him. I'll tell Mum what happened. How he was here and that I wouldn't speak to him and how I didn't let him into my room. That will make her happy." She knew she'd done the right thing, but why then did she feel so disappointed that Dad hadn't tried a bit harder to open the door. He wasn't that weak.

Erin lay on her bed and waited. Maybe he would come back. But he didn't. She picked up the phone, I'll ring Sonia she thought. Maybe we can meet up. Mum had given her a phone as a present for her birthday. It wasn't a mobile, which she had wanted, or her own line with her own number of course, but she had an extension in her room so that she could lie on her bed and talk to her friends in peace. Mum was so kind. She was just about to ring Sonia's number when she heard Dad's voice on the line, using the other phone.

Of course, she should have put the phone down straight away, she knew very well that she shouldn't listen to other people's telephone conversations, but she couldn't. She sat with the receiver stuck to her ear and hardly dared breathe, she was so afraid that Dad would hear she was listening on the extension.

Dad was talking to a woman. Of course, it had to be Her, the Horrible One who'd stolen her Dad.

"How are you?", asked Dad.

"Fine, thanks", answered the Horrible One. "But where are you? I thought you were going to Lynn and Erin's to collect those papers."

"Yes, I'm here now", said Dad. "Lynn's at work and Erin's locked herself in her room and doesn't want to speak to me."

"Of course she does", said the Horrible One. "You're her father. Whatever has happened between you and Lynn she still loves you. You must understand that."

"Yes, I know, I really want to believe that", said Dad, "but why is she avoiding me? She didn't want me to come and see her on her birthday and Lynn said things were bad enough without me making it any worse for her."

"Lynn should be ashamed of herself!", said the Horrible One, sounding really horrible now. "I can understand why you couldn't bear to live with a woman like that."

"Exactly", said Dad, "and now Erin doesn't even want to talk to me. But she's my daughter, can you understand how that feels? I love her more than anyone else."

"Yes, of course I do", said the Horrible One softly. "You will always love Erin. She's your daughter and always will be."

"But what if I never get to see her? I must be able to see her otherwise I'll go mad!"

The Horrible One laughed sadly. "I promise you that Erin loves you, even more than I do, no matter what she says. You have to believe that otherwise you'll just make everything worse than it already is. It's difficult for Erin, she loves both you and her mother and she feels that she has to choose between you, and she can't. But don't worry, you can be sure that she loves you."

"I hope you're right", said Dad sadly, "I'm leaving here now. Bye."He put the phone down.

Erin felt quite dizzy. She felt happy, sad and confused all at the same time. She heard Dad in the hall getting ready to leave and she rushed out of her room and into his arms.

"Hi Dad, I just wanted to say goodbye before you left."

33

Whose Fault – Mum's or Dad's?

Questions for Dad's story

1 Why does Erin lock herself in her room when Dad is in the house?

2 Why can't she stop herself from listening in to the telephone conversation?

3 Why does she think of her Dad's new partner as the Horrible One?

4 Does the Horrible One seem horrible? What do you think Erin thinks as she listens?

5 Why is Dad upset? Does he want to see her?

6 Why does Erin give her Dad a hug before he leaves? Is it good or stupid of her?

Whose Fault – Mum's or Dad's?

Questions for both stories

1 Is it possible to decide whose fault it is that Erin's parents are getting divorced? Is it important?

2 Can you help falling in love even if you're married?

3 Are adults always as grown up as children want to believe they are? Can children sometimes understand difficult things better than parents?

4 Does Erin have to decide between her mum and dad?

5 Some children might be afraid that their parents will divorce. If they do then get divorced, are things as bad as the children feared?

6 Children sometimes think they can do things to stop their parents from divorcing. What can they do? Does it help?

7 Can it sometimes be a child's fault if their parents divorce? Do some children think they're to blame?

8 Can young people really understand what their parents argue about? Should it worry you? Can you avoid worrying about it?

9 Is it possible to be really angry with someone but still love them?

35

Kind Old Mrs Carlson

Mrs Carlson

Old Mrs Carlson wanted to be kind. And she was wasn't she?

She loved coffee mornings and when it was her turn to invite everyone to her house she wanted all the children to come too. She always served cakes, buns and biscuits in huge amounts and home-made strawberry tart. Mrs Carlson loved to bake and the children were allowed to eat as much as they wanted. So yes, of course she was kind.

Unfortunately, she was beginning to realise that these days she didn't really understand children.

Perhaps it was because she had never had children of her own, although she had been a child herself once, even if it was a long time ago. But she did know that children shouldn't be cheeky and rude to grownups, especially when the grownup was going out of her way to be pleasant and kind.

Yesterday she had really gone out of her way to be generous so it couldn't have been her fault that everything went wrong. It must have been that Alex's fault.

Christine had brought her two boys with her and that was fine. Two-year-old Anthony was a real charmer but he didn't sit still for a moment, so it was impossible to talk in peace and quiet when he was around. Then there was his older brother Alex. How old was he now – nine? Ten? Eleven? Time passes so quickly.

She shivered when she thought of yesterday's coffee morning in the garden.

It had been a real failure, even though she'd set the table with her best tablecloth and her best tea service. Of course, the tablecloth had been a mistake, they hadn't even managed to sit down before Anthony had got cake all over it and then spilled his drink, but he was only little. But, there was no excuse for his older brother who grinned and said something cheeky like "Just sling the old rag in the washing machine." Rag! That rag was her grandmother's best embroidered tablecloth.

However, she'd tried to smile and asked him if he'd like some strawberry tart. The boy scoffed it down so fast it was a wonder he didn't get a stomach ache.

Then little Anthony had noticed her raspberry canes. Those raspberries were her pride and joy. She had spent hours on her knees, taking great care to plant two straight lines of raspberry canes as a border between the herb garden and the flower beds. It looked so neat, especially now that the juicy, dark red berries were hanging from the branches. She knew they needed to be picked soon otherwise the birds would get them or they would shrivel up, and she had decided to do it that evening. Then she would enjoy them with cream and a little sugar. She would treat herself. Is there anything more delicious than a giant bowl full of raspberries?

"Raspberries", Anthony shouted happily. "Pick raspberries."

"No!", she wanted to shout, like a spoilt child, "they're mine, don't touch them." But she couldn't say that. She really wanted to be a kind old lady so she smiled instead. "Do you want to pick the raspberries?", she asked the boys. "Yes, well just pick as many as you like, that will make me so happy."

The boys' faces lit up and they ran over to the raspberry canes. Their mother Christine protested a little but of course they didn't hear her. How many raspberries could a child's stomach possibly hold when it had already been stuffed full with cakes, buns and strawberry tart? Not many, surely, she thought, two or three little handfuls at most. She could treat them to that.

But my goodness! Little Anthony wasn't too bad, but that great big lad, he was like a swarm of locusts, and before she knew it he'd eaten half a row! He systematically cleaned cane after cane of berries. He was going to eat every single raspberry in only a few minutes and his mother hadn't noticed a thing.

No, it was just too much. She was going to have to stop him, even if she did want to be kind. So she went over to the little path, smiled her kindest smile and called "No more raspberries now, boys!"

That should have been clear enough, but still friendly. However, it was not clear enough for the big lad who turned round to argue and just kept on picking. She was forced to shout again, a little sharper this time, but still with a smile, "No more raspberries now!" (It was on the tip of her tongue to add that there were no more raspberries for such ill-mannered brats! But of course she didn't.)

At last their mother came over and the boys unwillingly stopped picking the berries. Mrs Carlson liked children. At least, she liked the ones who'd been brought up to know how to behave, but she could not bear Alex – what a greedy boy. There was nothing strange about that, was there?

Kind Old Mrs Carlson

Questions for Mrs Carlson's story

1 Did Mrs Carlson want to be kind? Was she kind?

2 Does she like children?

3 She seems to think that children should be polite to adults, especially when the adults are being kind and generous towards them. Is this reasonable or is she just old fashioned?

4 Was it cheeky of Alex to say that she could throw 'the old rag' in the washing machine?

5 Is it mean of her to want to keep the raspberries for herself?

6 Alex is ten, shouldn't he have realised that it was inconsiderate to eat all of the raspberries?

7 The coffee morning was a disaster. Whose fault do you think it was?

Kind Old Mrs Carlson

Alex

Alex thought it would be a good idea to go with Mum to Mrs Carlson's.

Mrs Carlson was nice and even if going to a coffee morning isn't how a ten-year-old boy dreams of passing his time it would do for a couple of hours. She was fantastic at baking and there was bound to be loads of freshly baked buns and cakes, there always were. She was sure to have made on of her strawberry tarts as well. When someone praised her famous tart she would usually say "Oh, something like this is easy to throw together, it only takes a few minutes. You just use ..." Yes, well, whatever it is you use!

Alex planned to eat as much as he could. You could do that at Mrs Carlson's. He would also give Mum a break and play with little Anthony so that she could talk in peace. Anthony was quite a cool two-year-old, at least in small doses, and he thought the world of Alex – which of course Alex found completely natural. If it became too boring later he could go on his bike round to the newsagents, some of his friends were sure to be there.

 Aunt Carlson had set the table in her garden, under the big apple tree. There was a freshly ironed cloth on the table and her best china, and coffee and juice and loads of buns and cakes and as usual a huge home-made strawberry tart. Apart from Mum and Mrs Carlson there were three other mums, but no other children.

"Great", thought Alex, "it's just me and Anthony."

Little Anthony – well, he ran straight for the cakes.

"Cakes", he said happily, and filled both his fists as well as his mouth.

"Anthony", said Mum crossly, "you have to wait until they are offered."

But Mrs Carlson just laughed kindly.

"It doesn't matter, children will be children", she said, "Don't worry – just help yourself."

Anthony crammed three biscuits into his mouth at once and sprayed out crumbs and dribble all over the table. Mum tried to brush the crumbs off the table and apologised about the mess on the tablecloth.

"Oh, that doesn't matter", said kind Mrs Carlson. "I can easily throw that old rag into the washing machine."

Then Mum tried to get Anthony to sit on her knee but it wasn't so easy. He wriggled and twisted and then before anyone knew it he had knocked his drink all over the table. Mum was so embarrassed.

"What are you doing Anthony?", she said really angrily. "What's got into you?"

"It fell", said Anthony wondering whether or not he should start to cry.

Alex wanted to make everyone feel better.

"You can just throw that old rag into the washing machine", he said.

"Of course", said Mrs Carlson with a forced smile on her face. "Washing machines are a great invention."

Everyone helped to mop up the juice with the napkins and Mrs Carlson brought out a nice clean tablecloth and finally they could begin.

Alex and Anthony finished first. The grown ups just talked all the time, unlike the boys who ate quickly and with great concentration.

"If you've finished you could go and play for a while", said Mum, with a pleading look in Alex's direction.

He didn't really like the way she'd said it, but he didn't say anything. Of course he would look after his little brother for a while. That was what she had meant but what was the best way to occupy him?

Anthony decided that for himself.

"Raspberries", he said, pointing happily. "Pick raspberries."

He had just spied two long rows of raspberry canes on either side of the little path which framed the flowerbeds so nicely. Tightly packed, and in straight rows, they were laden with delicious ripe raspberries.

Alex saw the problem immediately. No matter how kind Mrs Carlson was, she was bound to want the raspberries for herself. Alex would have done at any rate, but how was he going to get Anthony to understand that?

But Mrs Carlson really was incredibly kind. Her whole face beamed as she said to the boys that they could pick the raspberries – and that they could pick as many as they liked.

What a fantastic offer! There's almost nothing better than fresh, ripe raspberries.

Then Mum started to speak, "no, that's a shame", she said, "you can't let them …"

But Mrs Carlson had decided. "Just pick them and eat them", she said, "Just as many as you like, you'll make me very happy."

Well, thought Alex, if it's that easy to make this kind lady happy then we should make her really, really happy and he placed Anthony at the end of the raspberry canes nearest the house.

"We'll eat from both ends", he said to Anthony. "You start here and I'll start at the gate and we'll see who gets the furthest before we meet. I'll shout 'Ready, Steady, Go!' to start us off."

"Go!", said Anthony happily and started eating straight away.

"I'll give him a head start", thought Alex. "I'll easily win anyway", and he ran down to the gate, got down on his knees at the first bush and began.

He needed to be both quick and systematic. He picked with one hand and collected the berries in the other. One branch was just about enough to fill his hand. As soon as his hand was full he put the berries into his mouth and then started on the next branch while he was still eating.

They tasted heavenly. Well, almost, he thought, really he preferred strawberries as they were bigger and juicier. He didn't want to be ungrateful though, these would certainly do!

Little Anthony didn't stand a chance; he was still at the end of the row when Alex was on to his third bush. Alex just didn't have the right technique, but he was still only little.

Alex was about half-way down the first row and Anthony was pulling at some of the plants when suddenly Mrs Carlson came rushing over to them.

"Boys!", she said, with a steely grin. "No more raspberries now."

Couldn't the old lady see properly, wondered Alex?

"It's OK", he shouted back, "There are loads left. We haven't even started on the second row yet."

It probably wasn't very clear as he'd just shoved a handful of berries into his mouth but surely she must have heard him, or was her hearing as bad as her eyesight?

But Mrs Carlson just kept stubbornly repeating "No more berries now boys, come and sit at the table with us."

"But…" Alex tried to explain. This was crazy, he thought.

Then Mum joined in. "Alex and Anthony!", she bellowed. "Come over here now and sit down. I'm ashamed of you."

"No more berries!", repeated smiling Mrs Carlson, like an old record with a scratch in it. "There are no more berries."

She was absolutely crazy!

47

Kind Old Mrs Carlson

Questions for Alex's story

1 What did Alex think of Mrs Carlson at first?

2 What did he think later on?

3 Why does Alex eat so many raspberries? What is he trying to do?

4 Does Alex think she's mean when she stops them picking the raspberries?

5 In what way does Alex misunderstand Mrs Carlson?

6 Does Mrs Carlson have problems with seeing and hearing, or what was wrong with her?

7 Why is Mum angry?

8 Is Alex a thoughtful and considerate boy?

Kind Old Mrs Carlson

Questions for both stories

1 Mrs Carlson really does want to be kind to the boys but she makes a big mistake. What is it?

2 Alex wants to be helpful and polite, but still Mrs Carlson thinks he's inconsiderate and bad mannered. Why?

3 Sometimes it can seem almost as if adults have a secret language they use when they want to be polite and pleasant, a sort of code that children don't always understand. Mrs Carlson calls the tablecloth an 'old rag' but when Alex says exactly the same thing then he's being really rude. Why do you think that is?

4 If Mrs Carlson misunderstands Alex and thinks he's being rude why doesn't she say so? Then it could all be sorted out. Instead she gets angry, but smiles politely. Why?

5 "Eat as much as you like!", said Mrs Carlson. That's an adult code too. What does she really mean? And what does Alex think she means?

6 Another code is "No more berries". What does this mean to Mrs Carlson and what does Alex think it means?

7 Why do adults sometimes express themselves in a way that needs to be translated before children understand what they mean? It's easy to misunderstand when people seem to talk in code. Does it have any advantages?

8 Was the failure of the coffee morning just one person's fault?

Off with the Ref!

Thomas

At last! There it was!

Four seconds until the end of the match with the score at 3-3. The ball came straight at Thomas. Someone from the other team appeared and there was a hard tackle. Thomas was pushed – roughly – but he didn't give up. Suddenly the ball was there again and Thomas' reflex reaction was perfect. All he had to do was kick the ball and slowly, smoothly, and elegantly, almost as if it was teasing, the ball found a little spot to the left of the goalkeeper and rolled straight into the goaaaaal!

A clean goal from Thomas! His first goal of the season in five-a-side football and it was the deciding goal of the match. The goal that would ensure his place on the team in the future. He imagined a microphone being held front of him.

"Thomas, your deciding goal really came just at the right time, with only four seconds to go. What were you thinking as you kicked it in?"

"I didn't have time to think", laughed Thomas. "It was a completely automatic reaction. First I was tackled, but I stood my ground and suddenly the ball was there again, I saw the gap at the left-hand side of the goal and the next thing I knew there it was, flying into the net … It was easy really", he laughed.

"And how do you feel now?"

"Fantastic! Over the moon! Couldn't be better."

"Does this mean you'll definitely get a place on 6A's team now?"

"That's for Ben to decide", said Thomas shyly. "I was just playing as a reserve because Amrit had to go to the dentist. But it went well today, so…"

"Went well?", exclaimed the interviewer, "You saved the whole match, maybe even the whole season. Didn't you?"

"I'm not so sure about that", laughed Thomas. "We've got the final to go and 7B are a tough team. But I'm sure we can do it! I really believe that we can do it, if we can keep the spark alight from today's match."

"As long as you're there to score the goals", said the interviewer. "After today you must be in the final."

"That's for Ben to decide", repeated Thomas modestly, "but I don't suppose there'll be any problem. Then we'll beat them!"

"Is that a promise?", laughed the interviewer. "Do you promise to beat 7B in the final?"

"Promise!", laughed Thomas back. "But 7B are a really tough team. We mustn't underestimate them."

He paused for a moment. Then he said firmly, "Of course we'll beat them. Yes, that's a promise. Of course we'll win, after today's performance."

"And how many goals do you think you'll score in the final?"

"Two, maybe three or maybe even four. It just depends what's needed really. We are good under pressure."

"We noticed", said the interviewer, "Thank you Thomas. Today's man of the match and the new rising star in five-a-side football."

"At a time like this I'm allowed to brag", thought Thomas. Anyway, it wasn't as if anyone realised he'd just given a T.V. interview in his head. He was allowed to be happy.

What was happening now he wondered? The cheers from the crowd who had squeezed into the gym had stopped and now they were booing.

"Off with the ref! Off with the ref!", they were chanting.

Slowly, Thomas began to understand. Ben, the sports teacher, who was the ref had disallowed the goal. But how could he? There was no doubt about it, the ball had hit the left-hand side of the goal and rolled right to the back of the net. He must have been bribed!

"The goal was scored from inside the penalty area, so is disallowed", shouted Ben as he pointed at the goalposts and blew his whistle to restart the game.

Nothing much could happen in four seconds so the game went to sudden death. All the enthusiasm had gone out of 6A. Why should they play on when they'd already won? Suddenly, a big beefy guy from the other team got the ball and the next thing they knew it was at the other end of the gym. It sailed into the goal and straight into the net at the back. Stupidly quick! That was it, after only eight seconds of extra time! How bad can it get?

The 8As were in the final and the 6's could go and cry!

Ben must be completely blind, or he'd been bribed, or at least he was biased. He was going out with the older sister of one of the other team. No wonder he wouldn't allow Thomas' goal. He shouldn't have been allowed to referee the match, anyone could see that he was biased!

It was cheating! We shouldn't have to put up with it, thought Thomas, at least not in football, but, then again, cheating happens everywhere. Call himself a sportsman, a referee – Ben deserved to be banned!

Off with the Ref!

Questions for Thomas' story

1 Why does Thomas' goal mean so much to him?

2 Is it normal for someone to pretend they're being interviewed on TV?

3 Why does Thomas do it?

4 How do you think Thomas will feel, now that his goal has been disallowed?

5 Do you think he'll get a permanent place on the team now?

6 Should Ben be allowed to referee if his girlfriend is related to one of the other team?

7 Do you think Ben was biased? Do referees usually favour one team?

Off with the Ref!

Ben

Ben had studied the rules for five- a-side football the night before the match.

Not that it was necessary. He'd played the game so much himself and there weren't really that many rules to worry about anyway, but the boys took this tournament very seriously so his reputation depended on it.

Everything had to be right. They'd played lots of five-a-side football since Ben had come to Kentish School as a newly qualified sports teacher. Ben loved the game and he'd managed to pass his enthusiasm on to the pupils. This tournament had been a great success. He'd managed to get a team from every class in the school. At first he'd thought about having two tournaments, one for the older boys and one for the younger ones and then getting the winners from each group to play each other in the final. But then he decided against it – it would be no fun if the younger boys didn't stand a chance.

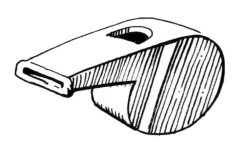

However, the younger boys had been confident. They'd asked for one big tournament for all the teams, and the fact was that most of the talent was in the younger classes, so why not give them a challenge? He let them have what they wanted.

Eventually, Ben would be able to pick the best players from each class and form a school team to play against other schools. And he was going to form a girl's team too. Someone as enthusiastic as Ben always had a lot to do.

Now it was the second semi-final and he had to concentrate.

In the first semi-final (against 5A) 7B had qualified for the final, and now 6A were playing 8B. Ben tried to be impartial (it wouldn't work otherwise, he said to himself), but secretly he hoped that 6A would win. Little David against the giant Goliath – of course you'd cheer for the smallest. Also, the boys in 6A had the right attitude, they were a tough team. Some of them would go far. You could see that already.

First, there was Amrit. It was such a shame that he couldn't play in the semi-final. He had a dental appointment at the same time. The boy himself was upset about it and Ben had even contacted Amrit's mum to try to get her to change the time. After all, it was the semi-final, but she wouldn't do it, no matter how much Ben tried to change her mind. They'd both been quite cross by the end of the conversation.

Ben had put Thomas in Amrit's place, a reserve who hadn't exactly done much to prove himself, but there wasn't anyone better. Even so, Ben still wanted to believe that 6A had a chance against the 8's. It would be so cool if they won, and with Amrit back from the dentist they would definitely have a chance against 7B in the final.

Ben liked the idea that a younger team might win the whole tournament. It would really show everyone that determination could win over strength in the end.

The lads in 6A were looking good. John scored the first goal in the middle of the first half. Then 8B equalised by the end of it, and in the second half dominated the whole game, first taking the score 2-1, and then 3-1. Being two years older makes a lot of difference at that age. Ben wondered if it had been a bad idea after all to have everyone in the same competition. Then, towards the end of the second half, everything changed.

6A had never played so well, even though Amrit wasn't there. Just a few minutes into the last period and the score was 2-3 and then 3-3. Sam, 6A's goalkeeper was really on form.

Everyone in the hall was jumping up and down with excitement, and the temperature in the hall was rising. The lads in 6A were definite favourites. All they needed was one more goal and they were really going for it, refusing to give up. The minutes were rushing by, just a few more seconds left until the whistle blew. Would there be extra time? Suddenly, everything seemed to happen at once.

One of the 8's tackled Thomas near the goal. Ben was about to blow his whistle, as they were both in the penalty area, but just as he was about to do so Thomas' foot came forwards and he kicked the ball straight into the back of the net. And there it lay!

Ben blew his whistle at exactly the same time as the ball went into the net. The crowd was roaring with happiness. Ben felt slightly confused. Thomas had been in the penalty area. Not by much, but enough for the goal to be disqualified. He thought about it for a while but was sure he was right so with a heavy heart he had to disallow the goal.

The crowd started booing and shouting "Off with the ref!" and Ben just had to put up with it, even though he thought it was very unsporting. Even worse than that was the sight of the happy 6A team becoming completely deflated.

Especially Thomas of course.

The whistle and the goal had come at almost the same moment. It took just eight seconds for Khalil in the 8's to score the deciding goal. He was a good player. It was a real shame for 6A, they really had deserved to win, but sadly, that's life.

Off with the Ref!

Questions for Ben's story

1 Do you have any similar competitions in your school? How are they organised?

2 Is it a good thing for the school tht Ben is paying so much attention to five-a-side football?

3 Is he biased in favour of one team or the other?

4 Do his feelings affect his judgement?

5 No-one except Ben noticed that Thomas was in the penalty area, so there would have been no protests if he'd allowed the goal, not even from the other team, but Ben disallowed it anyway. Why do you think this was?

Off with the Ref!

Questions for both stories

1 Only 8B were happy about the outcome of the match. Can anything good came out of it? What about for Thomas, for example?

2 Why was Thomas so sure that Ben was biased against his team?

3 Was Ben impartial?

4 If Ben was going out with the goalkeeper's older sister, would that be a good reason for him not to referee the match.

5 Sometimes, people say that rules are made to be broken. Would this include the rules of five-a-side football?

6 Cheating can be found everywhere, even in sport. Is it particularly important to get rid of it in sport? If so, why?

7 It's a shame for Thomas, he could at least have been given the triumph of scoring the winning goal. After the way things turned out, how do you think he will feel when he eventually calms down?

8 Is it important for Thomas to understand why the goal was disallowed (he probably hadn't realised his position when he scored)?

Stepbrothers

Peter

Peter had to buy a new photograph with his own money and he wasn't allowed to go out for a whole week!

He lay in his room feeling very depressed. *His* room, that was another thing, it had been his room until Mum and Dad had split up and Mum had moved out. Now he had to share it with Charlie.

It was one thing that Mum and Dad had divorced, at least now he didn't have to listen to them arguing all the time but now he lived one week with Dad in the old house and the next week with Mum. When he was with Mum it was just her and Peter, and that was really nice, but when he was with Dad, Trisha, Dad's new girlfriend, was always there too. And of course the dork, Charlie, her son, his 'new brother', as Trisha called him. More like 'pretend brother', Peter thought.

Charlie stayed with his own dad every other week too, but it was always when Peter was with his mum. "It's so your dad and I can be our own little family on our own sometimes", said Trisha.

"So that we avoid being with you", thought Peter.

Well, he was in favour of avoiding her too. Peter and Trisha agreed on one thing, at least. There was

no love lost between them. Charlie was worse. He and Peter had to share a room and were expected to be friends.

"You boys can have so much fun together. Peter, why don't you join the scouts too?"

They shared Peter's old room. It was a perfect room for one person, but far too cramped for two. Of course, it would have worked if he had been sharing with Chris, his best friend. Why couldn't Dad have fallen in love with Chris's mum instead?

Charlie was a real pain, he was sooo tidy. He had measured the room and drawn a line down the middle dividing his part of the room from Peter's. Talk about being fussy! Trish and Dad had thought it was such a good idea.

"Now there won't be any arguments about space, everything will be clear."

Plain stupid, Peter thought and took every opportunity he could to lie on Charlie's bed or sit at his desk. Whatever anyone said, it was his room!

It was while he was at Charlie's desk that this ridiculous thing had happened. A stupid little thing really, but the others didn't think so. Not even Dad. While Peter was sitting at the desk as usual he caught sight of a big photograph. It showed a grinning Charlie in his scout uniform wearing his little hat and scarf and his shirt with its little badges and that stupid belt. The whole works!

Peter hated uniforms on principal, why would a boy want to dress like that? But he did want to be fair to Charlie.

Charlie couldn't help the fact that he looked like a hamster, it wasn't his fault. No-one should be judged by the way they look (and if you want to collect sweets in your cheeks it's handy to look like a hamster). But he could help the fact that he was in the scouts. That was a choice he had made for himself.

Peter didn't know much about the scouts except that they were all stupid and pretended they were in the army or something. 'Be prepared' and 'I promise to do my duty to God', that's was their stupid motto, wasn't it? All they seemed to do was run around the countryside seeing who could kiss the most squirrels in ten minutes or something.

Peter had a felt-tip in his hand. Almost without him noticing, the pen drew a little moustache under Charlie's nose. It looked really good. His blond hair then became black with a little fringe that fell across his forehead. Then his front teeth became just a little longer and he grew some nice big round cheeks. Perfect! No, it's not your fault that you look the way you do, but your photo really should resemble you. Still, there was something missing. Maybe a little title for the picture! The photo was a full-length portrait, showing Charlie's shirt, trousers and sensible shoes, the whole works. The middle of the picture needed some improvement too.

Peter started to giggle. Then in clear felt-tip pen he wrote 'BE PREPARED' right across the middle.

By that evening Peter had already forgotten the whole thing, when suddenly Charlie came rushing in hugging the photo against his chest. He was crying like the big baby he was, even though he was eleven, like Peter. You don't cry at a little joke when you're eleven.

"Mum, look what Peter's done! He's ruined my scout photo!"

His mum looked, and hugged and tried to comfort him and then said, "This is disgraceful! I've had enough of you and your hooliganism!"

She didn't even look at Peter. She looked straight at his dad.

"Do you think he should get away with this? Are you going to let your son bully Charlie, because I'm certainly not going to!"

Dad looked really serious and grunted. Peter knew that he didn't think much of the scouts either, so he would probably just say that it wasn't that bad. A bit thoughtless maybe, but Charlie could always get another photo. Something like that. That's what he would have said in the old days when he was still allowed to think for himself and have his own opinion. But not these days!

Trisha held up the photograph and looked straight at Dad who looked really uncomfortable. Then he started shouting at Peter. Then he shouted some more. It was all to impress Trisha of course!

He wasn't going to put up with this kind of bullying, he shouted, and Peter would have to pay for a new photo out of his pocket money.

Of course, Trisha didn't think that this was enough, so Dad added that Peter was grounded for a whole week.

Punishment was one thing. Inside, Peter knew that what he'd done was a bit over the top. After all, it was Charlie's photo even if he had improved it. But what really upset Peter the most was the fact that Dad had been just as unfair and mean as Trisha and Charlie.

Stepbrothers

Questions for Peter's story

1 Is sharing a bedroom difficult? Do you share with someone?

2 Why does Peter think that sharing a room with Charlie is so difficult?

3 Is it ridiculous for Charlie to draw a line between the two halves of the room? Or is it a good idea?

4 Is it wrong of Peter not to like the scouts?

5 The felt-tip pen made a mess of the photo almost without any effort from Peter, so is it really Peter's fault?

6 Was it really such a bad thing for Peter to mess around with the photograph?

7 Peter thought that he'd improved the photo. What do you think?

8 Are Trisha and Dad right to say that he's being a bully?

9 What does Peter find the most upsetting thing about the whole event?

Stepbrothers

Charlie

Charlie hated himself when he felt the tears coming.

He really, really, really didn't want to cry, but this was just too much. He was sitting at his desk when he'd looked at the picture he had bought at scouts last night. He had spent nearly £10 but it was worth every penny, or he'd thought so at the time anyway. When his scout master had given him the photo, he had felt happy for the first time in ages.

Everyone at scouts had been photographed in their uniforms by a professional photographer, just like the one who took the school photographs. One group photo and then an individual one of each person. Now his portrait had been sabotaged.

Charlie remembered how happy he'd been the night before.

While Peter was asleep on his side of the room, Charlie had taken out his photo to admire it. It had turned out really well. The group photo wasn't

that great, just eighteen boys standing there in three rows, their faces were like small spots in the picture, but he could still recognise all his friends. He had only been going to scouts for a term, so he didn't know everyone that well, but Oliver was nice and he and Simon had spoken a few times.

Charlie had great expectations of the scouts. These are **my** friends, he thought, when he looked at the group photograph. This is **my** Scout Troop. He put the photograph back in the envelope and put it on the desk beside his bed. Then he lay and looked at the photo of himself.

That's really me, he thought. This is the real Charlie. Not the dork who's pushed around at school and bullied even more at home by his 'pretend brother', Peter. This is the real me, a happy eleven-year-old boy, strong and honest. Always prepared – someone who likes adventure and being outdoors. Perhaps he could even write 'Be prepared' at the top of the photo. He liked the idea but the photo was really too nice to write on. No, he would frame it so that it didn't get dirty and then he'd put it on his desk as a reminder of who he really was. Maybe he could put a sticker on the frame instead with 'Be prepared' written on it.

He held the photo with just the tips of his fingers around the edges, so that he didn't leave fingerprints on it. It was a really nice picture of a real scout who was smiling happily out at the world. His uniform was still brand new – his freshly ironed shirt with his scarf properly tied and his badge showing perfectly. Then he put the photograph back on the desk, turned off the light and fell asleep.

That was last night and now it had all been ruined.

Peter had destroyed his photo. Charlie was angry at himself for not having put it back into the envelope with the group photo before he went to sleep. But most of all he was furious with Peter. He'd used a felt-tip pen and drawn a moustache and black hair under his scout hat, and then made Charlie's front teeth longer and drawn really huge cheeks so that he looked just like a hamster. Then he'd written 'Be prepared' right across the middle. Charlie just couldn't hold back the tears.

He ran to his mum with the photo clutched to his chest and she was so kind to him. She hugged him and comforted him. She spoke to Peter's dad and told him he had to tell Peter off, which he did. Charlie was promised a new photo that Peter had to pay for with his own pocket money. That was only fair, but it didn't really help.

Why was Peter always so mean to him? That was the hardest part, Peter always seemed to want to hurt and upset him. Charlie had done what his mum had suggested, and had tried really hard to be friends with Peter. It wasn't his fault they had to share a room. Charlie would have happily slept in a cupboard under the stairs like Harry Potter if it meant he got a bit of peace. When Mum and Peter's dad said they had to share a room, Charlie had used a ruler and measured exactly where the border went, so they each had the same area, and at least Peter would have his own space. Charlie had even asked Peter if he wanted to join the scouts with him, even though he didn't really want him to. He did it to try and be friendly, but Peter had just burst out laughing.

Charlie didn't even know if he wanted a new photo, he didn't want to be a scout any more either. It wasn't just the photo that Peter had destroyed. Somehow Peter had managed to destroy a picture of a Charlie who didn't exist any more. A Charlie who was happy with his life – at least sometimes. How was it possible for so much to be destroyed with just one action? Now it felt like Charlie the scout was just as much of a dork as the Charlie at school, and the Charlie who had to share a room with his 'pretend brother', Peter. He was just a dorky idiot who looked like an ugly hamster in a scout uniform. Now every single thing was ruined.

Stepbrothers

Questions for Charlie's story

1 Have you ever felt as happy about something as Charlie did about his photo? What was it?

2 Why did Charlie like the scouts so much?

3 Why did he like the photograph so much?

4 When Peter drew on the photo what made Charlie feel the worst?

5 Why does Charlie think Peter spoiled the photograph?

6 Peter doesn't think he is a bully, but Charlie feels that he's being bullied by Peter. Who is right?

7 Why is personal criticism about your appearance or the things you like so hard to take?

Stepbrothers

Questions for both stories

1 Why do you think Peter dislikes Charlie so much?

2 Why doesn't Charlie like Peter?

3 Do people have to like their stepbrothers and sisters?

4 Both Charlie's mum and Peter's dad are trying to get the boys to be friends. Why isn't it working?

5 Will Peter's punishment help the situation?

6 Could their parents have done something else instead? What could they have done?

7 Can Peter and Charlie ever be friends? How could this happen and can their parents help them?

8 Is it necessary for the boys to be friends in order to avoid conflict in the family?

9 Would Peter's dad have laughed at the photo if Trisha and Charlie hadn't been there when he saw it?

10 How do you feel about groups like the scouts?

Daniel + Daniela = True Love

Daniel

Daniel had always loved Daniela, well, he had for the past three weeks anyway.

Had he somehow let his feelings show? No, yes, not directly – but maybe. Of course, he'd paid her lots of attention by foing things like hiding her gloves, sticking cheeky pictures on her locker and writing his 'tag' on her homework. Just the sort of thing you do when you're eleven years old and really like a girl.

So far, nothing had impressed her, she'd just rolled her eyes and tutted, and said, "Boys are such dorks!"

Her friends had done exactly the same thing, rolled their eyes, giggled, tutted and agreed that boys were unbelievably dorky.

He should have given up really, and maybe Daniela thought he had when he started to pay attention to her friends instead. Of course, that was only to make her jealous.

He seemed to stand a chance with Rebecca, Chloe and Ishani, so in one way it was working. They'd shrieked excitedly when he and Hassan had thrown their bags at each other, and said, 'Boys are such dorks'. Especially Daniel.

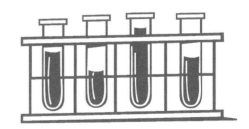

75

On the other hand Daniela took no notice, so in that way it wasn't working at all. Wasn't it obvious just from their names that they were meant to be together, that they were meant to be a couple? Daniel and Daniela, how clear could it be? It was as if they were a couple already. But not to her!

Daniel tried everything. He even climbed up to the second floor on the school's fire escape and hung like a monkey from one arm and waved with the other. The other girls all screamed with fear, but Daniela sat with her back towards the building reading. She didn't even look up, so he got down again.

That was before what happened in the science lab.

It was great fun as they were doing something really cool for a change. They had to mix hydrochloric acid with copper. The teacher told everyone that they had to be really careful, as it would bubble up like mad and produce a gas of some kind or other, or was it two gasses? The theory wasn't much fun but it was OK. Hassan had to record the different stages of the experiment as usual, and Daniel's job was to concentrate on how the test tube bubbled up like a witches' cauldron when he put the lump of copper into the hydrochloric acid. Wicked!

Even so, he wasn't ready for what happened. Daniel got such a shock that he jumped and knocked over his test tube which broke and the witches' brew spilled all over Daniela's hand!

She screamed really loudly!

At first everyone just stood there, stunned. By the time the teacher came running over Daniel had already grabbed Daniela by the shoulders, pushed her over to the sink and begun to run cold water over the back of her hand. He held her firmly by the wrist so that the water washed over the wound. He turned the tap on slowly, so that the water didn't rush out too hard and hurt her hand even more, but instead ran gently over the burn. Absent mindedly he rolled up her sleeve, which by now was soaked round the edges, but he didn't let go of her wrist for a moment, even though she wanted to pull her hand away from the water.

The cold water was obviously beginning to help, at least a little bit. She wasn't screaming any more, just sniffing a bit and she wasn't trying to pull her hand out of the water.

By now the teacher had got through. "Good", she said. "Cold water, lots of it, that's what's needed. Just keep rinsing it with water. What exactly happened here?"

"It was my fault", said Daniel, flatly. "I managed to spill the hydrochloric acid on her hand. I'm so sorry."

"Haven't I told you a thousand times…" began the teacher, but she really didn't have the energy to repeat what she'd already said a thousand times.

Instead, she shouted "Stop!" to the group who were just about to wipe the acid up from the bench with a piece of kitchen roll. "Don't touch anything. Move away from the bench. I'll clean everything up later."

Everyone backed away obediently. You could see how the acid was eating away at the bench, making a hole. It was still smoking a bit too.

Daniela was a little calmer now.

"How long should we keep rinsing it?" she asked in a weak voice.

77

"A long time", replied the teacher. "For about fifteen minutes or maybe a little longer, and then you will need to go to hospital and let them look at your hand there. It doesn't look too good."

It didn't look good at all. The acid had made quite a large burn on her hand, at least as big as a ten pence piece. Daniela was still crying, and Daniel just wanted to die. He felt so bad, and he couldn't believe that it was Daniela of all people that he'd hurt in this way. He wished a thousand million times over that he had spilled it over himself instead. Without him even noticing, tears were running down his own cheeks.

He was still holding Daniela's hand under the tap and without realising it he'd put his arm round her. Surprisingly enough, she didn't push it off. She was in shock.

Well, thought Daniel, that's the end of everything with Daniela. She's really going to hate me after this, forever. I can understand why.

"Daniela", the teacher said to her gently, "I think we can turn the water off now. I have a compress here that I'd like to put on the wound, then we will take you to casualty at the hospital and let them look at your hand. You can bring a friend with you. Who would you like to come?"

Daniela looked up at Daniel.

"Would you come with me?", she asked quietly.

Daniel couldn't believe it.

"If you wouldn't mind", she said. "Or some one else could …"

"Of course I will", said Daniel gruffly, "It's fine."

Daniel + Daniela = True Love

Questions for Daniel's story

1 Daniel pesters Daniela by hiding her gloves and writing on her homework. Is this what boys of around eleven or twelve usually do when they like a girl? Is it a good tactic, what might work better?

2 Do you think Daniela knows that he likes her?

3 Why does she act as if she doesn't care? Is she really not interested or is she just playing a game?

4 Why does Daniel think Daniela will hate him when he spills the hydrochloric acid?

5 Why does Daniela choose Daniel to go with her to the hospital?

6 Is it sensible to mess around and show off like Daniel does?

Daniel + Daniela = True Love

Daniela

Daniela realised she liked Daniel when he spilled the acid on her. Before that she thought he was just a dork. The world's biggest dork.

Well, probably no worse than all the other boys and maybe he messed around so much because he liked her. He hid her stuff, put up stickers on her locker, put his stupid 'tag' on her maths homework – just fooled around the whole time, he was ridiculous. But the other girls thought it was exciting.

"You must realise he's in love with you. It's really sweet. Why don't you encourage him a bit otherwise he'll just get tired of you." Girls can be almost as stupid as boys she'd thought. Almost, but not quite.

He broke his own record when he climbed up the fire escape outside the school and began acting like an ape – it was really dangerous. He hung from one arm, kicked away from the fire escape with his legs and waved with his other arm. He was on the second floor too, it was completely senseless!

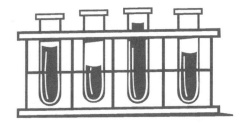

It made her feel really uncomfortable. Even if he was the last person in the world that she'd ever fall in love with, she didn't exactly want him to die because he was showing off to her! It was all so unnecessary.

Rebecca, Chloe and Ishani had roared with laughter just as he'd hoped they would, but Daniela pretended she hadn't seen him. Then luckily he climbed down. That was before the science lesson.

And that was when she realised how much she liked him.

They were doing an experiment to see what happened when hydrochloric acid was mixed with small pieces of copper. Unfortunately, the girls had ended up right next to Daniel and Peter. It was quite difficult to pay attention to what you were doing as the boys were showing off and you really needed to concentrate. The acid was very corrosive and the teacher had gone on and on about how careful they had to be.

Daniela had very steady hands as she carefully poured a small amount of the acid into a test tube. The girls then made a cone out of paper and put the copper inside it. Then, very carefully, they placed the paper cone over the test tube and let the copper pieces glide into the acid. It started bubbling like mad and smelled really bad, just like it was supposed to.

The boys were pushing and shoving, but Daniela took no notice until suddenly Daniel jumped back and it felt as if someone had poured liquid fire over the back of her hand. Without even thinking about it she screamed!

Daniel had stupidly managed to knock over the acid and it had gone all over her hand, and it was so painful! Before she knew what was happening she felt Daniel take her by the shoulders and steer her over to the sink. He turned on the tap and held her hand firmly under the water.

She tried to pull her hand away, it hurt when the water hit the burn, it was really painful, but Daniel refused to let go. Slowly, she began to realise that the cold water was making it feel at least a little better. She wasn't really crying any more, just sniffing and sobbing a bit.

Daniel turned down the tap and held her hand so that the water didn't fall directly onto the burn but instead hit her hand just above it and ran over the burn, washing it. That felt better.

She noticed that her sleeve was soaking wet but she didn't have the energy to do anything about it. Daniel had obviously noticed it too and he pulled her sleeve up with his other hand. By now the teacher had reached them.

"Good", she said. "Lots of cold water. That's what you need, just keep rinsing it. What actually happened here?"

Daniela couldn't say anything but Daniel said it was entirely his fault, he'd spilt the acid on Daniela.

"Haven't I told you a thousand times ..." began the teacher.

Daniela was glad she didn't finish the sentence. What was the point of telling them off? You could see that Daniel was really upset. Daniela wanted to comfort him.

The teacher's attention then turned to the rest of the class to make sure that there were no more accidents. They were just about to wipe up the acid with kitchen paper, how stupid can you get? Daniela was feeling much calmer now.

Her hand was still painful, but at the same time it was nice that Daniel was being so kind to her. He had put his arm round her shoulders, she liked that. He was like a completely different person! He was no longer the stupid dork who was always messing around, but a kind, considerate boy who was really upset because he'd accidently hurt her.

She looked up at him slowly and she noticed that he was crying. That was when something happened to Daniela; she felt a burning sensation, not in her hand, that didn't feel too bad any more, but inside. Daniela really liked Daniel! They stood there for a long, long time and rinsed her hand.

After a while, the teacher said they'd rinsed her hand enough and put a compress on it and said that Daniela should go to casualty. Who did she want to go with her?

"Would you mind coming with me?", she asked quietly, looking at Daniel.

Daniel looked really confused, "Yes, if you want me to …" (Had she been wrong? Didn't he like her after all?)

Daniel cleared his throat. "Of course I will, that's fine."

Daniel + Daniela = True Love

Questions for Daniela's story

1 Could Daniela have liked Daniel all along but just not admitted it to herself? Why might this be?

2 Do you think Daniela was impressed by Daniel's behaviour on the fire escape?

3 Why might she not have liked him all along?

4 Daniel has been showing off in the lesson. Does Daniela think this causes the accident?

5 How does Daniela show that she is starting to like Daniel?

Daniel + Daniela = True Love

Questions for both stories

1 What sort of things do boys do to show that they like someone?

2 What sort of things do girls do?

3 Why did Daniel think he was in love with Daniela?

4 What made Daniela decide she liked Daniel?

5 When people behave badly or stupidly, what reasons might lie behind this behaviour?

6 If someone behaves stupidly on one occasion, does this affect how people view them at other times?

85

The Psychopath Test

Joe

Joe had failed the test.

It was cool to have a test that you didn't have to pass. It made a change to have a test that you could be proud not to have passed, instead of feeling stupid.

Joe's older brother (who was really clever) hadn't passed it either and now Joe was going to try it out on his friends.

A group of them were standing in the playground enjoying the spring sunshine, four girls and three boys from his class. The perfect group to experiment on!

Joe jogged over and came to a stop in front of the group. "Have you done the psychopath test?" he called over to them. It wouldn't be the same if one of them already knew about it, but no-one did.

"What, you mean you can test yourself to see if you're a psychopath?"

"I know I'm OK", said Joe, "I've already done it and I'm fine, but what about you? Does anyone dare to take the test?"

"What do you have to do?" asked James, who was quite a nervous person.

"You just have to try to solve a problem", explained Joe casually.

"What sort of problem?"

"A sort of detective mystery", said Joe.

"What's that got to do with psychopaths?"

"You'll see", said Joe secretively. He thought for a while and tried to remember the story.

"Right! There was this girl at her grandmother's funeral."

"How old was she?", asked Amy.

"I'm not sure, not that young, maybe about eighteen. At the funeral she noticed this really handsome man."

"Did she fall in love with him?", asked Anne.

Joe looked at her, "I don't know", he said. "She just saw him from a distance in the church, you can't fall in love that quickly."

"I often do!", said Anne laughing. "From a distance and then as soon as I get close and talk to them I get over it!"

Joe was getting annoyed. "It's not your love life that we're testing now ..."

"Why not?", laughed Anne, "You might turn out to be quite interested."

"Go on", complained Karim, "What happened next?"

"Well, the man didn't go back to the house afterwards, so she never actually met him and no-one she asked knew who he was either." He paused dramatically.

"Then, a month later she murdered her older sister", he said darkly, "but she was never caught. The question is, why did she murder her older sister?"

"Why not?", asked Freddie, "Big sisters are a real pain."

"You don't know that she thought that," said Anne.

"All girls are a pain", said Karim.

"No they're not!", said Amy and Niamh at the same time.

"No, but if you think about it …", Niamh was beginning to get interested in the problem. "It must have had something to do with the boy in some way."

Joe nodded.

"I know, she fell in love with the boy and then found out that it was her sister's new boyfriend and she became crazy with jealousy and she murdered her sister. What about that?"

"That doesn't make sense", said Leo critically. "You can't fall in love with someone to that extent from a distance."

"Not with you anyway", said Niamh, and the others laughed.

"That's not right", said Joe. "She wasn't jealous, nothing like that."

"Perhaps she was upset with her sister because she'd inherited the grandmother's money", suggested Leo.

Joe shook his head.

"It's enough to know that the older sister was murdered", Freddie went on. "I know what pests they can be."

"You're not even close", said Joe in a superior voice. "Not even close."

Freya was the only one who hadn't said anything. She was a pretty, quiet girl, a bit shy sometimes. She was always very organised and always had the right pens and books she needed for her lessons. She was clever too. She never made a big deal out of it, but if a difficult question was ever asked in class she was usually the one who knew the answer.

She looked a bit uncertain, but she began "I'm not sure. It sounds a bit stupid ... but maybe she wanted to see the boy again and she thought if her sister died then maybe when she was buried he would turn up for her funeral. Or is that too stupid?"

"Absolutely right! Congratulations Freya!", shouted Joe happily. "You've passed the test, you're a psychopath!"

"What is a psychopath?", asked Freya uncertainly. "I sort of know, but..."

"They are often intelligent and charming people", said Joe, "who have absolutely no conscience at all. Psychopaths know the difference between right and wrong but they just don't care, because they're so clever they can avoid getting caught out. Only a psychopath could pass the test. It's been scientifically proved that normal people couldn't even imagine a situation where someone would commit a murder just so that they could meet a handsome boy at the funeral."

Everyone was laughing and started teasing Freya.

"Any new murders in the pipeline?"

"What about the headmaster? Lots of handsome boys are sure to turn up to his funeral. We won't tell!"

"What a really cool test", thought Joe, "and it's great that it was know-all Freya who fell into the trap!"

The Psychopath Test

Questions for Joe's story

1 Do you know what a psychopath is?

2 Do you think you can be certain that someone is a psychopath?

3 Is Joe right when he says that it's been 'scientifically proven' that the only people who can solve the problem are psychopaths? Why does he say it?

4 Do you think anyone really believes that Freya is a psychopath just because she passed the test?

5 Do you think Joe is being a bully or do you think he's just teasing in a friendly way?

6 What's the difference between teasing a little for fun and bullying?

7 Why did Joe think it was especially good that Freya passed the test?

The Psychopath Test

Freya

At last it was nearly summer.

Freya was standing in the playground with a group from her class, soaking up the sunshine. There were still a few minutes of sunshine left before the bell would go for the end of break. Great! Then along came Joe and stopped front of them.

"Have you done the psychopath test?", he called.

No, no-one had heard of the psychopath test but Freya thought it sounded interesting. A psychopath was a clever person who was absolutely deadly because they had no conscience. They were the type of person who used people without caring about their feelings. If you wanted a career as a terrorist it would be an advantage to be a psychopath because you wouldn't have a conscience to stop you. Freya felt uncomfortable. Normal people could be mean and stupid sometimes, but people who were thoroughly cruel – that was awful! How would you recognise them?

She was curious about the test. Joe told them a sort of mystery story. An eighteen year-old girl was at her grandmother's funeral, where she caught sight of a handsome young man who she wanted to get to know, but he disappeared right after the funeral and no-one knew who he was. A month later the girl murdered her older sister but she was never suspected of the murder. The question was, why did she do it?

Everyone thought about it.

Freddie thought that older sisters were such a pain that it was no wonder that she was murdered. He said it at least three times. Freya laughed to herself. Little brothers like Freddie weren't that easy either and Holly, Freddie's sister, was really nice.

Amy decided it must be about jealousy. If the girl knew that her older sister was going out with the handsome young man then perhaps she wanted her sister out of the way.

A bit of a long shot, thought Freya. The answer must be in the story we've been told and it didn't say anything about the sister knowing the man. Quite the opposite, no-one the girl asked knew who the man was and she must have asked her own sister.

Leo started to wonder about the inheritance. Quite clever really, thought Freya. If the grandmother was rich and the older sister inherited the whole lot then maybe the younger sister could inherit it from her. Unfortunately that had the same problem as the jealousy theory. It wasn't mentioned in the story. The story was about a handsome young man, not an inheritance. The young man had to be part of the solution otherwise why would he be mentioned at all.

Freya tried to think logically, and then she giggled to herself. It seemed so stupid, but it seemed to be the only possible answer if you looked at all the facts.

A little nervously she told the others her idea because it sounded so unlikely.

"Maybe she wanted to see the man again and the only way she could think of it happening would be if her sister died and there was another funeral in the family, and maybe he would come to that. Or is that too stupid? "

"You're absolutely right!", shouted Joe. "Congratulations, you passed the test, you're a psychopath!"

The gang cheered.

Freya smiled nervously, she felt both proud that she'd passed the test but at the same time she was a little confused. Surely it didn't mean she was a psychopath just because she got it right. Or maybe she was wrong about what a psychopath was. So she asked Joe, just to make sure. Sure enough it was just what she'd thought. A psychopath was often very clever, and Freya knew she was clever. They were completely without conscience as well. But surely that wasn't true about her?

"Only a psychopath could pass the test", said Joe. "A normal person would never even dream that someone would commit a murder just so that they could meet a handsome man at the funeral. It is just too crazy for anyone but a psychopath to even think of – it's been scientifically proven."

Everyone laughed and started teasing Freya.

"Any new murders in the pipeline, Freya?" "What about the headmaster, lots of handsome boys would come to his funeral?" "We won't tell anyone!"

At first she tried to laugh with them. They weren't being mean, they were just joking. But what if they were right?

"Who am I really?", thought Freya to herself. "No one else passed the test, just me. No-one else managed to think in such a twisted way. Perhaps I am a psychopath but just don't know it. Joe did say it was scientifically proven that only psychopaths could pass the test."

"Am I really so insensitive?", she wondered. "Do I have a clever brain that lacks the normal feelings that other people have? Is that why I don't have a boyfriend? I think I'm quite pretty but still no-one has asked me to be their girlfriend. Is it because they feel a chill coming from me? It's not the sort of thing you can ask anyone either. How would I put them right if they did think that?"

She did have feelings because she knew she quite liked Joe. He was really clever and knew so much, but he certainly wouldn't want to be friends with a psychopath.

Freya felt terrible.

"Who am I?", she whispered to herself. "Who am I really?"

The Psychopath Test

Questions for Freya's story

1 Do you know what a psychopath is?

2 Would it be easier to be a terrorist if you're a psychopath?

3 Freya thinks that she doesn't have a boyfriend because she's a psychopath. Can you think of a more simple explanation?

4 What would you have said if Freya had been your friend, and she'd asked you if you thought she was a psychopath?

5 Were Freya's friends being unkind to her?

The Psychopath Test

Questions for both stories

1 Did you work out the answer and pass the 'Psychopath Test'?

2 Can the test be taken seriously?

3 Why does Freya take the test seriously?

4 Is it normal for some to people wonder if they're different in some way?

5 Could you ask someone if they think you're different? Who would you ask?

6 If someone told you they were worried that they were different, how would you react?

Why are You so Disorganised?

Karen

It was Saturday morning, the day of the riding test.

Karen was quite nervous because they would have to show everything they had learned. Everyone had to wear one of the smart jackets with the riding school's crest on it (at least those people who had managed to persuade their parents to buy them one, otherwise you just had to wear what you had), everyone had brown jodhpurs and black boots and a riding hat, so it would all look really good.

"All you need to do is show that you can trot, canter, turn and jump and all that sort of thing", said Dad. He didn't really know anything about riding, but at the moment Karen was more worried that she didn't know much either. Imagine what would happen if Treacle didn't do what she wanted and tried to do his own thing!

What would she do then? She was feeling really nervous but was quite excited as well.

She had hardly slept last night and when she did sleep she dreamt that she had arrived too late because she couldn't find her riding clothes. Someone had spread them all over

99

the house and then she missed the bus and she was really panicking, it was awful.

There was no chance of that really happening though, she had everything under control. She had a special place in her wardrobe where she always kept her riding stuff. On the left hung her jacket (completely new and unused) and her jodhpurs. Her boots, all cleaned and shining stood underneath (she always cleaned and polished them as soon as she got home from riding, it was easiest). She always hung her riding hat on a hook when she wasn't using it and on the floor underneath was a special bag holding all the brushes and other things she needed for the stables. So it never took her more than a few minutes to get her things together and be ready to leave for the stables.

There was lots of time; Karen always made sure she had lots of time because she really hated being rushed. First though, she was going to call for Louise, who had been her best friend since nursery school. Lou was the one who'd introduced her to horses and riding and they spent all their free time together collecting pictures of horses, talking about horses and laughing about things that had happened at the stables. They had the same sense of humour too, so they really were best friends.

There was only one thing about Lou that she couldn't understand. How could anyone be **so** disorganised? Not that it really affected Karen much, but it was hard to understand.

Karen rang Lou's doorbell at half-past nine and as the test didn't start until twelve they had loads of time. She'd counted it back in her head to see how much time they'd need. If we get there by eleven, then I'll have an hour to get Treacle groomed and put his tack on and get changed myself as well. The bus takes twenty minutes, and it's a ten minute walk from the bus to the stables. We might have to wait ten minutes or so for the bus, so that makes forty minutes altogether. So if they left Lou's at twenty-past ten they would be in perfect time. That meant they had fifty minutes to spare.

"Hi", said Lou, "are you here already? It doesn't start 'til twelve, does it?" She looked a bit unsure.

"Don't worry", said Karen, "It does start at twelve."

Lou laughed, relieved. "Good", she said. "I'm not ready yet. I need to eat something first. Would you like anything?"

Karen said no thanks, she'd already had breakfast.

Lou got some juice and put a couple of slices of bread in the toaster.

"Where are your mum and dad?", wondered Karen.

"They've gone to the supermarket", said Lou. "Come on, I've got something to show you."

She pulled Karen by the arm. "Look what I got for my birthday, isn't it fantastic?"

In her bedroom, on the shelf, was a large glass tank. A special lamp had been rigged up between some large books and in the tank was a small lizard curled up in a flower pot. Lou took it out.

101

"I'd like to present Morphus, he's called a bearded dragon. Isn't he sweet?"

Karen had to think for a moment, did she really think the lizard was sweet? Slowly, she was brave enough to let it creep up her arm. Yes, it was quite sweet after all.

Then a strong smell began to spread through the house and suddenly the smoke alarm started to beep loudly.

"Oh no! The toaster!", cried Lou, and she put the lizard on the bed and ran down to the kitchen.

Karen put the lizard back in the tank and closed the lid, then followed her. The kitchen was thick with smoke. The toast was burnt black, and the girls had to open the windows to clear the air and then put more bread on to toast.

"Where's the peanut butter?", mumbled Lou. "It was here a moment ago."

She searched through all the cupboards and Karen helped her by looking in the fridge.

"Not it there", said Lou. "It's too cold in the fridge for peanut butter."

"Well, it's here anyway", said Karen. She glanced quickly at her watch.

"We should go soon", she said worriedly.

"We've got loads of time", said Lou, "it's only ten past ten. We've got almost two hours."

"We'll have to groom the horses and get changed and anyway we have to get there first. We really need to leave in about ten minutes."

"We've got loads of time", said Lou again, but she pushed the rest of the toast in her mouth, gulped down her juice and got up from the table all in one movement.

"Finished!", she said happily. "I just need to get my things."

But that was easier said than done. As soon as she was back in her room and saw her unmade bed she gave a shout of alarm.

"Morphus! Oh no, where are you? Where are you Morphus? You haven't run away have you?"

"I put him on the bed", she explained to Karen, "and now he's gone. He could be anywhere, you'll have to help me look. He's great at climbing. Yesterday he climbed up the curtains and it took me hours to find him."

"Look in the tank", said Karen calmly.

"No", said Lou, crossly, "I didn't put him there, I put him on the bed when I smelt the toast burning."

"I put him in the tank", said Karen. "Hurry up now we should have left five minutes ago."

Gradually, they found Lou's riding hat in the hall cupboard, her grooming kit under the bed, her jacket in the washing basket and her jodhpurs over a chair in the living room, but they couldn't find the riding boots anywhere. Then Karen remembered she'd seen them outside the front door.

"I'll have to brush them", said Lou anxiously. "They're all muddy!"

"You won't notice from a distance", said Karen telling a white lie. "We really have to leave, we're going to be late."

They raced to the bus stop and just caught the bus. Lou had left her bus pass at home so Karen paid her fare. At the very last minute Treacle and Cinderella, carrying two very flustered girls, joined the end of the line of horses.

"We made it!", whispered Lou, smiling happily.

Karen didn't smile back.

"Why are you so disorganised?", she hissed angrily.

That made Lou angry too.

"If I am, it's my problem", she hissed back. "It's nothing to do with you."

They rode out into the paddock each as angry as the other.

Karen hated to be rushed, she would get a tummy ache from worrying. She knew she would forgive her best friend for making the morning so rushed and spoiling the whole day, but she had to let her know how horrible it was and how angry she felt. She couldn't just pretend it hadn't happened. That was asking too much.

It was only several hours later, when the girls were back at Lou's house and playing with Morphus that they really stopped feeling angry with each other.

Why are You so Disorganised?

Questions for Karen's story

1 Why does Karen dream that she can't find her riding kit and she'll be late?

2 What advantages are there for Karen in being well organised?

3 Is it easy or difficult to plan like Karen? Why?

4 Why is Lou late?

5 Is it unkind of Karen to complain about Lou being disorganised?

6 Whose fault is it that the girls are angry?

Why are You so Disorganised?

Louise

The riding test at the stables was going to be great fun!

Lou's best friend Karen was going to call for her. They'd been best friends since nursery, and now they were nine and still in the same class together. Lou hoped that everyone in their group had managed to persuade their parents to buy them one of the riding jackets with the crest on. It would look really good if they were all dressed the same.

She was going to ride Cinderella as usual and she'd put some sugar lumps in her pocket for her favourite horse. Karen would be riding Treacle.

The door bell rang. Mum and Dad must have forgotten something, they'd only just left to go to the supermarket. No, it was Karen. Why was she here already when there were several hours to go before the test started?

"Hi, you're here already, cool. It doesn't start until twelve though does it?", Lou immediately began to worry that she'd got the time wrong.

"No, we've got plenty of time, it doesn't start until twelve", Karen replied.

Lou laughed, relieved.

"That's good, I'm not ready yet. I need to eat something first. Would you like anything?"

But Karen had already eaten breakfast.

Lou put a couple of slices of bread in the toaster. It was really old and was a huge thing that you had to watch all the time otherwise it burnt the toast. The toast didn't pop up automatically any more. She got out the peanut butter and some juice.

Then she remembered Karen hadn't seen her present. The brilliant, fantastic birthday present she'd got a week after her birthday because Mum and Dad hadn't had time to organise it beforehand. She took Karen's arm and dragged her into her bedroom.

"Come on, I've got something to show you. Look what I got for my birthday. Isn't it great?"

In her room on the shelf stood a brand new tank and a special lamp that shone in and warmed the small lizard. Lou took it out.

"I'd like to present Morphus, a real bearded dragon. Isn't he sweet?"

Karen looked a bit scared but then she let him creep up her arm. Suddenly the smoke alarm went off and at the same time they could smell burning coming from the kitchen.

"Oh no, it's the toaster", shouted Lou and rushed into the kitchen.

The toast was completely burnt and the girls started coughing from the smell of the smoke. They opened all the windows and eventually the smoke cleared and the alarm stopped beeping.

Karen seemed anxious and kept saying she wanted to leave, but Lou at least wanted to have some breakfast first. She made some more toast (and kept an eye on the toaster this time) spread it with peanut butter and drank her juice. When it was time to go Lou suddenly shouted with fear.

"Oh no! Morphus, where are you? You haven't run away have you?"

She'd just remembered that when the smoke alarm had gone off she'd put Morphus down on the bed and rushed into the kitchen, and now he was gone.

Lou turned to Karen. "He could be anywhere, he's really good at climbing. Yesterday he disappeared up the curtains and I was looking for him for hours. Please help me look for him."

She simply had to find Morphus. Imagine if he managed to get outside and froze to death. They didn't have time for this, it was time to leave. She was almost in tears. Why did this always happen? Karen just sat on the bed and looked snooty.

"Look in the tank", she said in a superior voice.

"No", said Lou in despair, "I didn't put him in there, I know I put him on the bed when the smoke alarm went off."

"I put him in the tank", said Karen. "Now hurry up, we should have left five minutes ago."

Lou should have been happy, but actually she was a bit annoyed. Karen could have told her straight away instead of trying to make a point.

Now where was her riding hat? And her jodhpurs? And her jacket, who'd taken it? She hunted for ages before she found it in the dirty washing basket. Oh yes, she'd spilled ice-cream on it and it still hadn't been washed. She'd just have to wear it anyway. This morning everything was going wrong. Where were her riding boots? Not in the hall, not in her wardrobe, not under the bed or in the bathroom. She couldn't find her stupid boots anywhere.

Finally, Karen told her that she'd seen them by the front door, and even though they were all muddy she wouldn't let Lou brush them, she just kept going on about how they needed to hurry up.

They ran for the bus and Lou was so stressed that she forgot her bus pass and had to borrow the money from Karen. When they joined the line of horses at the very last second Lou smiled at Karen.

"We made it!", she said triumphantly.

"Why are you so disorganised?", hissed Karen.

That made Lou really cross. The morning had been bad enough without Karen pointing out how perfect she was. Both girls ended up sulking – for several hours.

Why are You so Disorganised?

Questions for Lou's story

1 Can Lou help being the way she is?

2 Why is she late? Is it her fault?

3 The girls arrived on time, so why is Karen so angry?

4 Might it feel worse for Lou as she is the one who finds it hard to be organised? Should it bother Karen?

5 How does it feel if someone only ever tells you what you've done wrong and not what you've done right?

Why are You so Disorganised?

Questions for both stories

1 Karen and Lou remember things about their day differently. Think of an example of this. What does it tell you about the girls that they remember or leave out these details?

2 It is easy to see that you might have problems if you were like Lou, but are there any advantages to being like her?

3 It is clear that Karen likes to organise and plan ahead, but might it have some disadvantages?

4 Why are the girls almost late?

5 The girls usually get on really well together but when they fall out Karen thinks that Lou's hopeless and Lou thinks that Karen is stuck-up. Who do you think is right?

6 Are we stuck with the way we are or can we change things about ourselves? Is it really possible to pay attention and be more organised or is that just what parents and teachers want us to believe?

7 Does nagging from parents and teachers ever help?

8 What should Karen and Lou do in the future to make sure they stay friends?

9 What should you do if you are more like Lou than Karen?

10 What should you do if you're more like Karen?

Parents' Evening

Jack

Jack hadn't exactly been looking forward to parents' evening and it was turning out just as he'd feared.

Everyone was so worried. His teacher, Miss Murray, was worried. Mum and Dad were worried because Miss Murray was worried and Jack was worried because everyone else was worried. Miss Murray did most of the talking.

"You see", said Miss Murray, "Jack is a very nice boy, he's not naughty in any way, he's not rude or unpleasant in any way, but he dreams. He sits and daydreams all the time. He's late all the time, even after break and he never has his books with him or his pen. And he never hands in any written work." She smiled sadly at Jack, "Do you recognise yourself here?"

Jack smiled sadly back at her. "I'm not always late", he said, "and I don't always forget my books and it's not true that I never hand anything in."

"But it's often true", said his teacher. "Why?"

"My work doesn't come out the way I want it to", he said. "But I always hand in the tests, the important things."

115

"But everything is important", said Miss Murray.

"How does he do in his tests?", asked Dad. "Does he do well in his written work?"

"Yes, he does do quite well in his tests."

"I usually get 70 or 80 percent", said Jack.

"Well, that sounds quite hopeful", said Dad.

"Yes, but school isn't just about passing tests", said Miss Murray, sounding a little cross. "The most important thing about school is being a part of the lessons and Jack doesn't join in with the rest of us. He sits lost in his own thoughts."

"I hear more than you think", said Jack.

"Well, that's good", said Miss Murray doubtfully, "but you do daydream a lot don't you? Am I right?"

Jack nodded.

"Why is that? Don't you enjoy school?"

"I don't know", he mumbled.

"Speak up", said Miss Murray brightly, "and take your hand away from your mouth when you talk."

"I don't understand why we have to go to school", said Jack. "I think the most important thing is that I learn things by reading, and from TV programmes and the internet, and talking to my brother and Mum and Dad. Why do I have to go to school?"

Miss Murray kindly tried to explain why he had to go to school.

Jack looked out of the window.

The conker tree had just begun to flower. Yes, he did sit lost in his thoughts because they were, quite simply, more interesting. The teacher just went on about things he already knew, most of them anyway, over and over again, slowly, slowly so that everyone understood. He couldn't say that to her, of course. Why would he want to upset his teacher, after all, she was doing her best.

He smiled to himself.

Like learning that in French a dog is 'le chien', and instead of just telling them that, even though everyone knew it already, the whole class would have to say 'le chien' together for about fourteen days. Then they'd have to write a whole book full of 'le chien'. The next month they'd do the same with 'la table', and anyone who hadn't finished writing 'le chien' would have to finish it at home and the teacher would worry about the kids who hadn't managed to keep up. Well, not quite, but it was almost that bad.

"... so you have to understand why we're worried about you", finished off Miss Murray and looked at Jack. "Don't you think so Jack?"

Jack sat up.

"Yes, of course", he said uncertainly.

"You were off daydreaming again", said Miss Murray sadly. "What were you thinking about?"

Jack didn't want to tell her.

So instead he said, "That people say there was no such thing as time before the Big Bang. Matter can only exist in time and the Big Bang happened when a little clump of matter, about the size of a ping-pong ball, exploded and created the whole universe. But surely that ball must have existed in time? Or did it appear from nothing and then time come later? How can something come from nothing? I don't really understand."

Miss Murray looked a bit confused.

"Big questions", she said. "That's the sort of thing you learn if you study philosophy at university when you are older."

"Astrophysics, actually", said Jack.

"But if you want to go to university then you have to work hard in school now."

Jack had promised himself he'd be polite, but now he became quite angry.

"So you mean I'm going to have to wait years and years before I can get an answer? It's a long time. I might as well look it up on the internet, it would be easier."

"Maybe he's upset about something", said Mum. "Don't you like school? Is someone being mean to you?"

"I like my friends and I like the breaks", said Jack. "It's just the lessons that are boring."

Miss Murray changed the subject.

"The fact that you never – almost never – have your books with you and …"

"If she says pen one more time, I'll bite her on the arm", thought Jack to himself.

"… or a pen", continued Miss Murray, "Why's that do you think?"

Jack decided not to bite her arm. Instead, he looked worried and thoughtful.

"I had lost some of my books", he said. "I've got new ones now, but sometimes I forget to bring them to school."

Miss Murray looked at him as if she'd just discovered something really important.

"Jack, you should say to yourself as soon as it's break time, 'I've got maths next and I need my maths book and my pencil case, with pencils and a rubber.' Get them all ready before you go into the playground, then you'll always be prepared for your next lesson."

"Give me break, please", thought Jack, "You mean you want me to think about my lessons even in the playground? That's the only free time I have."

"But what if I've left my stuff at home?", he asked instead.

He realised it wasn't a very good answer, but Miss Murray seemed delighted.

"Yes", she said happily, "Every morning you must ask yourself 'What lessons do I have today? What do I need to take with me today?' Then pack your school bag, of course it would be even better if you packed your bag the night before."

"I've lost my school bag", said Jack.

"We can buy a new one", said Mum quickly.

"You need to have some structure", said Miss Murray happily. "Then everything will be much easier. What do you think, Jack? Doesn't that sound like a good idea?"

"Maybe", said Jack, sullenly.

"Excellent", said Miss Murray, enthusiastically. "Then you'll find everything is much more fun at school."

"We'll help you!", said Mum and Dad, sounding almost as enthusiastic.

"So, shall we try it?", asked Miss Murray happily.

Jack took a deep breath. "Now they are going to make me think about school even when I'm not there", he thought sadly.

"Don't you think it's a good idea Jack? Jack?"

Jack gave a small smile.

"Yes", he said quietly into his hand. "It's a good idea."

Parents' Evening

Questions for Jack's story

1 What is Jack's problem?

2 What is Miss Murray's problem?

3 Would everything be OK for Jack if people stopped worrying about him?

4 Jack points out that Miss Murray says he is 'always' late instead of saying he is 'often' late. Does it make a difference?

5 Miss Murray suggests that he should plan things in advance, pack his bag the night before and get things ready at break time. Is this good advice?

6 Why doesn't Jack like her ideas?

7 Does Jack understand what Miss Murray means?

8 Does Miss Murray understand Jack?

9 Do you recognise yourself in Jack? What for example?

10 How would you solve these issues?

Parents' Evening

Miss Murray

Miss Murray had really wanted to avoid parents' evening with Jack and his parents. Most of the time she liked teaching and she felt she coped quite well, but not with Jack. She just didn't understand the boy.

She sighed. She wanted to get through to Jack and this was her chance. She really did want to understand how he thought and felt, and when she did get through to him she was going to explain how she and the other teachers saw the situation.

She didn't want to argue with him, because then he'd just clam up. No, she wanted to show him that she cared and that she really was worried for his sake.

He was a skinny boy who was already utterly bored at school. If he had been a teenager it would have been a bit different, that could be a difficult time emotionally, she knew that. It was pretty normal for teenagers to be tired and bored and to have mood swings, she could deal with that. But Jack hadn't reached that stage yet.

He wasn't a trouble-maker with too much energy either, she could usually deal with pupils like that too. No, he didn't distract anyone else, he just didn't seem to care. He came slinking in late every day, mumbling excuses, sat in his seat and began staring out of the window. Of course, he never had his books or pens with him. If she asked where they were, he would say they were at home or that he'd lost them.

Was he unhappy? Maybe he was being bullied? Did he have problems at home? Something had to be wrong! The boy was unhappy about something and Miss Murray wanted him to be happy.

Parents' evening started going wrong almost straight away.

Miss Murray described how he was always late, and forgot everything, and daydreamed the lesson away. Then she smiled at him. "Do you recognise yourself?" He replied that he wasn't 'always' late, but admitted that perhaps he was 'often' was.

She was tempted to reply that he might be on time for one day in ten, but without his homework, and then one day in ten he had his homework with him but was late. She was prepared to bet he hadn't been on time and had his pens and books with him for a single day that whole term.

Instead, she stayed calm, changed 'always' to 'very often' and smiled. Then she asked why he 'never' … sorry, 'hardly ever' handed in any class work. He'd write a few lines, rub them out and then throw his work in the waste paper basket. Why did he do that?

"It never turns out the way I want it to", he said. "But I always hand in tests, the important things."

This made her angry, but she tried not to show it. It wasn't his job to decide which pieces of work were important and which weren't.

"All school work is equally important", she said shortly.

His dad then wanted to know how Jack did in his tests. Of course, he did quite well in them, surprisingly enough, and that was good, but as she tried to explain the most important thing in school was joining in during lessons and Jack didn't. It wasn't enough just to do well in tests.

"I usually get 70 or 80 percent", said Jack. Did he really? She wasn't entirely sure about his marks in all of his tests, but on the other hand she didn't think he had any difficulty understanding. But he did have difficulty concentrating during his lessons.

Then she actually seemed to make contact with Jack.

"Don't you like school?", she asked. And then he answered. He didn't understand why he had to go to school, he said. He thought he could learn everything he needed to know from watching television or from the Internet.

"OK", she thought, "He's only a child, he is allowed to be immature." So, instead of being sarcastic, she tried to explain from a teacher's point of view why school is actually more important than ever in today's society.

"Ask your mum and dad", she said happily. "We all still go back to the classroom every now and then to extend our knowledge, otherwise we can't keep up at work." Then she noticed that Jack had gone back to staring out of the window, completely gone!

"You've disappeared again", she said sadly. "What are you thinking about?"

He said something muddled about space and the Big Bang. He couldn't have dreamt of anything further away from school if he'd tried.

Now she felt she had to encourage Jack and be positive. She said that he could learn about such things when he got to university, but he had to get through school first.

His mother wondered if perhaps he was being bullied, but he wasn't, he said. He liked his friends and he enjoyed break times, it was just the lessons that were so boring.

Miss Murray was beginning to get a headache. She started to try and end the meeting on a positive note. 'Structure' was the key word. Think about what you need for school the night before and get your things together then. Structure your day! Plan in advance! So obvious, so easy. But sometimes we have to state the obvious.

She thought she saw a glimmer of light behind his eyes when she said that. The simple things are often the best.

"Don't you think that's a good idea, Jack?", she said persuasively. "Jack?" She smiled hesitantly.

"Yes", he said quietly. "It's a good idea."

Parents' Evening

Questions for Miss Murray's story

1 Miss Murray really wants to understand Jack and help him, why is it so difficult for her?

2 She's also angry with him. Why is this?

3 Why does she try not to let Jack know that she's angry with him? Is that a good or a bad thing?

4 Is everything at school equally important? Why does Miss Murray say that it is?

5 Jack wonders why children have to go to school, but when Miss Murray tries to explain he doesn't listen. Why is that?

6 What is Miss Murray' advice to Jack? Is it good advice?

7 Does Jack think it's good advice, do you think?

Parents' Evening

Questions for both stories

1 Miss Murray wants to understand Jack, why is she being so unsuccessful?

2 Does Jack want to understand Miss Murray? Is it possible for him to understand her?

3 Jack actually gives Miss Murray two chances to understand him, but she misses both of them. What does he say that gave an opportunity for them to make contact? How does she miss the chance?

4 Is Miss Murray a hopeless teacher?

5 Is Jack a hopeless pupil?

6 Why does Miss Murray get a headache?

7 Could Jack be happier in school generally, not just at break time with his friends?

8 What could be done to improve things for Jack? What could the school do? What can Jack do for himself?

9 Why do we have to go to school?

10 What would your ideal school be like?

Stories for seeing life from different perspectives
Lars Collmar
Translated by Lesley Gleeson

These innovative books consist of pairs of stories which describe an everyday situation from two different viewpoints. Each of the two stories is followed by questions that will stimulate lively discussion, designed to illuminate the perspectives and feelings of the different characters in the stories. Once both stories have been read, a final set of questions allows groups to compare the experiences of both characters.

Covering everyday issues encountered at school, in families and with friendships, and ideal for use by teachers in PSHE discussions and also by SLTs and therapists this easy-to-use resource provides an excellent tool for working in this sometimes difficult area.

WALKING IN THE SHOES OF ANOTHER

'Do not judge another until you have walked a mile in his moccasins.'
Native American Proverb

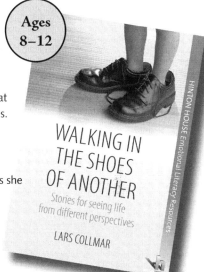

Ages 8–12

The stories in this volume are intended to encourage younger children to try seeing the events that happen around them from different perspectives and to try to understand other people's emotions.

Ten stories are told from two different perspectives. Events that might seem unfair, strange or untrue can appear completely different when seen from the viewpoint of someone else.

- When an old lady encourages two young boys to help themselves to her raspberries, why does she then get upset when there are none left?
- Why would a little boy be so thoughtless that he gets chocolate on his classmate's new dress?
- When mum and dad separate, should their daughter have to decide who is to blame?
- A boy is wrongly accused of shoplifting, why might the shopkeeper act as he does?

2010 ♦ 140pp ♦ photocopiable paperback ♦ 978-1-906531-24-9

SEEING THROUGH THE EYES OF ANOTHER

'You never really understand a person until you consider things from his point of view – until you climb in his skin and walk around in it.'
Atticus Finch, in Harper Lee's *To Kill A Mockingbird*

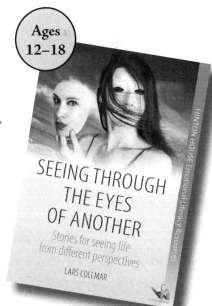

Ages 12–18

In this volume, the author provides stories that illustrate 15 events, themed for older youngsters, from two different perspectives.

- A boy and girl both exaggerate the retelling of their first date, but in what ways do their accounts of the story differ, and why?
- A girl asks her friend for an honest opinion about her singing, but when she is told the truth she is devastated. Would it have been better to tell a white lie?
- A boy is asked by his dad if he has taken some missing money, how do both the accuser and the accused feel in this awkward situation?
- A teenage girl wants to stay over at her boyfriend's house, but her parents forbid it, even though her mum remembers doing the same herself. Is she being a hypocrite? How do they reach a compromise?

These pairs of stories show how an event that initially seems clear-cut becomes more complicated when viewed from someone else's perspective. In a simple and clear way the author shows how all stories have more than one side and the importance of not jumping to conclusions or being too quick to judge.

2010 ♦ 200pp ♦ photocopiable paperback ♦ 978-1-906531-25-6

info@hintonpublishers.com ♦ www.hintonpublishers.com

The Communication Toolkit

Assessing and Developing Social Communication Skills in Children and Adolescents

Belinda Medhurst

The Communication Toolkit is a practical collection of user-friendly resources designed to support young people aged 8 to 16 who have social and communication difficulties. It draws on a variety of theoretical backgrounds including emotional literacy, solution-focused and social-use-of-language approaches.

The accessible worksheets cover subjects such as self-concept & self-esteem, body language & facial expressions, awareness of self and others, relationship skills, conversational & listening skills, feeling safe and staying in control.

- Provides a valuable assessment tool and indicator of key areas for improving social and language skills.

- Illustrated worksheets with are accessible to those with language and learning difficulties.

- Professionals can focus on areas on concern and explore the young person's view of themselves and others through an individualised communication programme.

- Addresses key areas of SEAL and can be used in primary and secondary mainstream as well as SEN settings.

- Contains guidance and notes for professionals as well as photocopiable worksheets.

Through structured activities youngsters will be helped to develop emotional literacy, self-esteem, social understanding and ultimately behaviour and communication skills.

A varied and appealing resource that teachers, SLTs, SENCOs, psychologists and behaviour support workers will find invaluable for use with an older age group not always addressed in social skills materials.

2009 • 206pp • A4 photocopiable paperback • ISBN 978-1-906531-26-3

info@hintonpublishers.com • www.hintonpublishers.com